FUTURE
English for Results
2

MULTILEVEL COMMUNICATIVE ACTIVITIES BOOK

Sarah Lynn

Series Consultants

Beatriz B. Díaz

Ronna Magy

Federico Salas-Isnardi

PEARSON
Longman

Future 2 Multilevel Communicative Activities
English for Results

Pearson Education, 10 Bank Street, White Plains, NY 10606

Staff credits: The people who made up the *Future 2 MCA* team, representing
editorial, production, design, and manufacturing, are Rhea Banker,
Elizabeth Carlson, Nancy Flaggman, Irene Frankel, Margot Gramer,
Michael Kemper, Michael Mone, Liza Pleva, and Barbara Sabella.

Cover design: Rhea Banker
Text design: Wanda España
Text composition: TSI Graphics
Text font: 13 pt. Minion
Illustrations: Steve Attoe, pp. 37, 95; Kenneth Batelman, pp. 49, 51; Laurie
Conley, pp. 3, 7, 77, 87, 115; Stephen Hutchings, pp. 27, 67, 107; André
Labrie, p. 47; Anna Veltfort, p. 17

ISBN-13: 978-0-13-199150-7
ISBN-10: 0-13-199150-7

PEARSON LONGMAN ON THE WEB

Pearsonlongman.com offers online
resources for teachers and students. Access
our Companion Websites, our online catalog,
and our local offices around the world.

Visit us at **pearsonlongman.com**.

Printed in the United States of America
1 2 3 4 5 6 7 8 9 10—DME—14 13 12 11 10 09

Contents

Unit 7 Health Watch

Unit 8 Job Hunting

Unit 9 Parents and Children

Unit 10 Let's Eat

Unit 11 Call 911!

Unit 12 The World of Work

Introduction

Welcome to *Future 2 Multilevel Communicative Activities Book*.

The ***Future 2 Multilevel Communicative Activities Book*** contains 60 communicative ready-to-use reproducible activities. Each activity corresponds to a lesson in the Student Book and recycles the vocabulary, language structures, and themes of that lesson. The activities are a valuable addition to the class, focusing on fun and communication while helping students internalize the new target language.

Each activity is accompanied by detailed teacher notes that guide the teacher and provide suggestions for adapting the activity to multilevel students in the same classroom. Very little teacher preparation time is needed, and the only additional materials needed are a photocopier and a pair of scissors.

What makes the activities in the book communicative?

All of the activities require students to communicate effectively to accomplish a task. The task may be to share information with a partner to complete a bus schedule or to circulate around the classroom to ask fellow classmates about their weekend plans. The activities are highly structured ensuring that students always know what they need to do and how close they are to accomplishing the task.

What makes the activities multilevel?

Adult Ed ESL classrooms are by nature multilevel. Many factors—including the students' age, educational background, and literacy level—contribute to the student's level. In fact, the same student may be *at level* in one skill, but *pre-level* or *above-level* in another. The greatest challenge for a teacher of a multilevel class is to keep all the students engaged all the time, drawing on their strengths and supporting them through their weak areas.

The teacher notes include Multilevel Options so teachers to adapt the activities for pre-level and above-level learners. They offer specific ways to provide the pre-level students with additional scaffolding for extra support, and to challenge the above-level learners to work more independently and to extend the activity.

How do the activities engage all of the students?

The activities in this book are designed to engage learners in a number of ways. First, nearly all the activities integrate all four language skills: speaking, listening, reading, and writing. Second, the activities involve different learning modalities. For example, many activities have students move as they learn and will appeal to kinesthetic learners. Many activities require students to interpret graphs, maps, game boards, and pictures and will appeal to visual learners. Third, the activities encourage students of all levels to contribute. The responsibilities for a task are distributed so that everyone must participate and everyone must give feedback. No students are left out. All learners contribute what they can based on their strengths and receive the multilayered scaffolding support to help them in their weaker areas. Because the activities are highly interactive and dynamic, they provide learners with many opportunities to negotiate meaning and check comprehension. This keeps the class humming with energy and purposeful communication.

Overview of Activity Types

Activity	Grouping	Task
Board Game	Small Groups	Students play a board game that reviews unit theme, grammar structures, and vocabulary.
Build a Sentence	Pairs	Students assemble words and phrases into meaningful sentences.
Find Someone Who	Whole-Class Mixer	Students ask their classmates questions in order to complete a series of sentences.
Information Gap	Pairs	Students ask and answer questions in order to find missing information in everyday print formats such as receipts, bus schedules, weather maps, and job applications.
Interview	Pairs	In sustained conversation, students ask each other a series of questions and report their findings to the class.
Matching Game	Whole-Class Mixer	Students ask and answer questions about their cards to find the correct match.
Miming Game	Pairs	Students give clues to words by acting out their meaning.
Mix and Match: Conversations	Pairs	Students work together to find questions and responses to make three (or more) different conversations.
Picture-based Story	Whole Class and Pairs	Together the class composes a story based on a picture that reflects on one of the unit's themes.
Put in Order	Pairs	Students read sentences and work together to put a conversation or a story in the correct order.
Question and Answer Game	Small Groups or Pairs	Students ask and answer questions using visual cues such as a map or realia in the classroom.
Survey	Whole-Class Mixer	Students ask their fellow classmates a question and report the results.
Tic-Tac-Toe	Small Groups	Teams play the classic game with a new twist; they must compose correct questions about their classmates to score a box in the grid.

About the Teacher Notes

Teacher Notes

Teacher Notes provide the teacher with all the instructions for the Activity Master on the facing page:

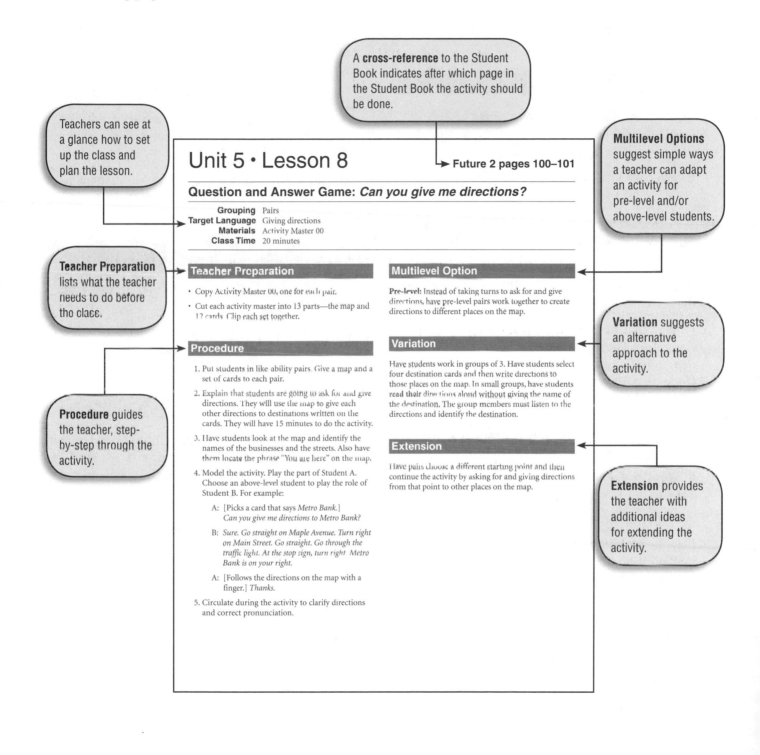

A **cross-reference** to the Student Book indicates after which page in the Student Book the activity should be done.

Teachers can see at a glance how to set up the class and plan the lesson.

Multilevel Options suggest simple ways a teacher can adapt an activity for pre-level and/or above-level students.

Teacher Preparation lists what the teacher needs to do before the class.

Procedure guides the teacher, step-by-step through the activity.

Variation suggests an alternative approach to the activity.

Extension provides the teacher with additional ideas for extending the activity.

Unit 5 · Lesson 8

▶ **Future 2 pages 100–101**

Question and Answer Game: *Can you give me directions?*

Grouping Pairs
Target Language Giving directions
Materials Activity Master 00
Class Time 20 minutes

Teacher Preparation

- Copy Activity Master 00, one for each pair.
- Cut each activity master into 13 parts—the map and 12 cards. Clip each set together.

Procedure

1. Put students in like-ability pairs. Give a map and a set of cards to each pair.

2. Explain that students are going to ask for and give directions. They will use the map to give each other directions to destinations written on the cards. They will have 15 minutes to do the activity.

3. Have students look at the map and identify the names of the businesses and the streets. Also have them locate the phrase "You are here" on the map.

4. Model the activity. Play the part of Student A. Choose an above-level student to play the role of Student B. For example:

   A: [Picks a card that says *Metro Bank.*]
   Can you give me directions to Metro Bank?

   B: *Sure. Go straight on Maple Avenue. Turn right on Main Street. Go straight. Go through the traffic light. At the stop sign, turn right. Metro Bank is on your right.*

   A: [Follows the directions on the map with a finger.] *Thanks.*

5. Circulate during the activity to clarify directions and correct pronunciation.

Multilevel Option

Pre-level: Instead of taking turns to ask for and give directions, have pre-level pairs work together to create directions to different places on the map.

Variation

Have students work in groups of 3. Have students select four destination cards and then write directions to those places on the map. In small groups, have students read their directions aloud without giving the name of the destination. The group members must listen to the directions and identify the destination.

Extension

Have pairs choose a different starting point and then continue the activity by asking for and giving directions from that point to other places on the map.

Picture Match: *What do they look like?*

Grouping	Whole-class mixer
Target Language	Describing physical characteristics, *be* and *have* in the simple present
Materials	Activity Master 1
Class Time	20 minutes

Teacher Preparation

- Copy Activity Master 1. Make two copies of Activity Master 1 if you have up to ten students, or four copies if you have up to 20 students.

- Cut each copy into six cards.

Procedure

1. Give one card to each student at random. Have students look at the picture of the two people on the card.

2. Explain that students are going to walk around the classroom. They will describe the two people on their card in order to find a matching card. Tell students not to show their cards to anyone. They will have 15 minutes for the activity.

3. Write the following question on the board:

   What does the woman look like?

   What does the man look like?

4. Have students look at the pictures and describe how the two people look.

5. Play the part of Student A. Look at your card. Walk around the classroom. Ask an above-level student to play the part of Student B. Ask the questions on the board. Continue to call on above-level students until you get a match.

6. To give students more support, write the following model sentences on the board:

   She's <u>tall</u>.

   She has <u>short</u> <u>curly</u> <u>brown</u> hair.

   He's <u>bald</u>.

   He has a <u>goatee</u>.

Note: Remind students that they should continue to question students until they find a match.

7. Circulate during the activity to make sure students are not showing anyone their cards and are forming correct sentences.

8. When students find a match, give each student another card to continue the activity.

Multilevel Options

Pre-level: During the activity, allow pre-level students to refer to the model on the board.

Above-level: Tell above-level students to do the activity without looking at the model on the board.

Extension

After the class has finished the activity, have students sit with a partner who has a different card. Have pairs look at both pictures and talk about how the people in their pictures are different. For example:

> A: *In my picture the woman has short curly brown hair.*

> B: *In my picture, the woman has short straight brown hair.*

Picture Match: *What do they look like?*

Build a Sentence: *Describing People*

Grouping	Pairs
Target Language	Describing physical characteristics and personalities, compound sentences with *and / but*
Materials	Activity Master 2
Class Time	20 minutes

Teacher Preparation

- Copy Activity Master 2, one for each pair of students.

- Cut each copy into 20 cards. The white cards are sentence beginnings and the gray cards are sentence endings.

  Note: You may want to start with only the first five pairs.

- Clip each set of cards together.

Procedure

1. Put students in like-ability pairs. Give a set of cards to each pair.

2. Tell Student A to shuffle the white cards and Student B to shuffle the gray cards. Have students put their cards face up on their desks.

3. Explain that students are going to work together to make ten (or five) correct sentences with the cards using the connector *and* or *but*. Tell students that the white cards are sentence beginnings and the gray cards are sentence endings.

4. Model the activity. Assemble a white card and a gray card into a correct sentence and read it aloud: *My brother is talkative but I am quiet.*

5. Write the sentence on the board. Tell students to assemble the sentence with their cards.

6. Tell students to continue to assemble correct sentences. There are ten correct sentences.

7. Circulate during the activity to make sure students' matched sentences are correct.

Multilevel Option

Pre-level: Give pre-level students only the first five pairs of cards so that they have fewer choices to consider as they match the cards. When they finish the first half of the cards, give them the second half.

Extension

If some pairs complete the activity before the rest of the class, have partners take turns picking up a card and saying the sentence and continuing it with *and* or *but* and then adding their own ending. The other partner writes the sentence down and corrects it if necessary.

Variation

Mixer: Use one copy of Activity Master 2. Give each student a card at random. Have students walk around the classroom. They continually say their half of the sentence until they find the matching half. If there are more than 20 students, use two copies of Activity Master 2.

Build a Sentence: *Describing People*

1. My brother is talkative	but I am quiet.
2. My brother has blue eyes	but I have brown eyes.
3. My brother is short	but I'm tall.
4. My brother is cheerful	but I'm moody.
5. My brother is bossy	but I'm laid-back.
6. My brother isn't average height	and I'm not, either.
7. I'm a student	and my brother is, too.
8. I'm not heavy	and my brother's not, either.
9. My brother has straight blonde hair	and it's short.
10. My brother is kind	and I am, too.

Picture-based Story: *Learning Styles*

Grouping	Pairs and then whole class
Target Language	Learning styles
Materials	Activity Master 3
Class Time	25 minutes

Teacher Preparation

Copy Activity Master 3, one for each student.

Procedure

1. Give a copy of Activity Master 3 to each student.

2. Explain that students are going to write a story based on the pictures.

3. Put students in cross-ability pairs to discuss the questions on Activity Master 3.

4. Have students report their ideas to the class. Make sure students understand the scenes:

   (1) Marcos is studying at home. It isn't a good place for him to study. There is too much noise.

   (2) Marcos is practicing English with some classmates. He's learning better this way. He likes to talk and listen when he learns.

5. Ask the class: *What's the story?* Have the class develop a story line orally.

6. Have students dictate the story line. Listen to students' ideas, repeat the ideas while rephrasing them in correct English, and write them on the board.

7. Have students copy the story in their notebooks.

Multilevel Option

Above-level: After they copy the story, have above-level students write comprehension questions about the story to ask the class.

Extension

- After the class has finished the activity, erase words from the story and have students tell you the missing words.

- Dictate a sentence from the story and have students write it down. Then write the sentence on the board so students can check their work. Repeat with other sentences.

Picture-based Story: *Learning Styles*

- Where is Marcos studying?
- Is this a good place for Marcos to study? Why or why not?

- What is Marcos doing?
- Is this a good way for Marcos to learn English? Why or why not?

1. **PAIRS: Discuss the questions under each picture.**

2. **CLASS: Tell the story to the teacher.**

Tic-Tac-Toe: *Questions with* Be

Grouping Groups of 4
Target Language *Be: Yes / No* questions and short answers, personal questions
Materials Activity Master 4
Class Time 20 minutes

Teacher Preparation

Copy Activity Master 4, one for every four students.

Procedure

1. Make sure all students know each other's names. You may want them to wear name tags during this activity.

2. Put students in like-ability pairs. Each pair is a team. Put two teams together to play the game. Give each group of 4 a copy of Activity Master 4.

3. Explain that students are going to play Tic-Tac-Toe with true questions and answers about their classmates. Students on each team will create a correct question that can be matched with a true answer in the grid. Here are the rules:

   • A student on Team 1 points to an answer in the grid (for example, *Yes, he is.*) and then asks a question (for example, *Is Jacob tall?*). Since the true answer is, *Yes, he is*, Team 1 marks an X over that answer in the grid.

   • Team 2 takes a turn by pointing to an answer and asking a question. If the question and answer are correct and true, Team 2 marks an O over the answer in the grid.

   • The first team to get three marks in a row— vertically, horizontally, or diagonally—wins.

4. Circulate during the activity to make sure that students' questions are grammatically correct and that the answers are true.

5. Have teams play a second round.

Multilevel Option

Above-level: Have above-level students write the questions while they play the game.

Extension

If some groups finish before the rest of the class, have each pair write two questions for each answer.

Tic-Tac-Toe: *Questions with* Be

Round 1

No, he's not.	No, they're not.	Yes, they are.
No, she's not.	Yes, he is.	Yes, we are.
Yes, she is.	No, we're not.	Yes, it is.

Round 2

Yes, we are.	No, it's not.	No, they're not.
No, we're not.	Yes, it is.	Yes, they are.
Yes, she is.	Yes, he is.	No, he's not.

Board Game: *Personal Information Questions*

Grouping Groups of 4
Target Language Describing physical characteristics and personality, *be:* affirmative and negative questions
Materials Activity Master 5, a coin, two markers for each group
Class Time 20 minutes

Teacher Preparation

Copy Activity Master 5, one for every four students.

Procedure

1. Put students in like-ability pairs. Each pair is a team. Put two teams together to play the game. Give each group of 4 a copy of Activity Master 5, a coin, and two markers.

2. Explain that students are going to play a board game. Here are the rules:

   • Pair 1 flips a coin to move. *Heads* means the team moves the marker ahead two squares and *tails* means the team moves their marker ahead one square.

   • Pair 1 moves the marker to a square. Student A forms the question. Student B answers with true information. Pair 2 listens to make sure Pair 1's question and answer are correct.

   • If Pair 1's question and answer are correct, Pair 2 takes a turn.

   • If Pair 1's question and answer are incorrect, Pair 1 moves the marker back one square, and Pair 2 takes a turn.

   • If a pair lands on a square that already has a marker on it, the pair gets to move forward one square.

   • The first pair to reach FINISH wins.

3. Circulate during the activity to make sure students' answers are correct.

Extension

If some groups finish before the rest of the class, have each pair write three true sentences about their partner. For example:

> Louis is from Haiti.
>
> He's shy and quiet.
>
> He's a visual learner.

Answer Key

1. What do you do?
2. What is your last name?
3. Are you a student?
4. What is your brother or sister like?
5. What is your address?
6. What is your country like?
7. Where are you from?
8. Is your hair long and wavy (wavy and long)?
9. What is your learning style?
10. Are your eyes green?
11. Are you shy and quiet (quiet and shy)?
12. What are you like?
13. Are you from China?
14. Is your hair short and curly (curly and short)?

Board Game: *Personal Information Questions*

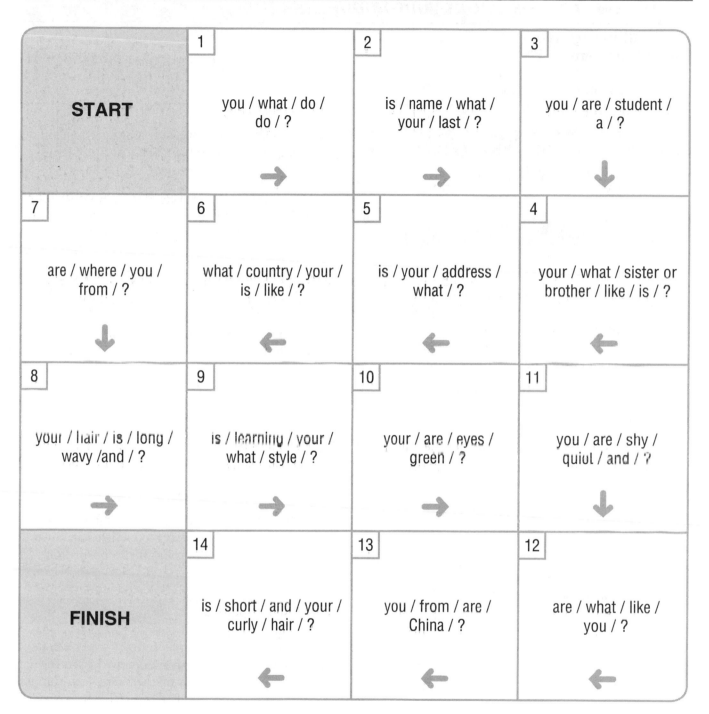

	1 you / what / do / do / ? →	2 is / name / what / your / last / ? →	3 you / are / student / a / ? ↓
START			

7 are / where / you / from / ? ↓	6 what / country / your / is / like / ? ←	5 is / your / address / what / ? ←	4 your / what / sister or brother / like / is / ? ←

8 your / hair / is / long / wavy /and / ? →	9 is / learning / your / what / style / ? →	10 your / are / eyes / green / ? →	11 you / are / shy / quiet / and / ? ↓

	14 is / short / and / your / curly / hair / ? ←	13 you / from / are / China / ? ←	12 are / what / like / you / ? ←
FINISH			

Unit 2 • Lesson 3

Interview: *Tell me about your family.*

Grouping	Pairs
Target Language	Family
Materials	Activity Master 6
Class Time	25 minutes

Teacher Preparation

Copy Activity Master 6, one for each student.

Procedure

1. Give a copy of Activity Master 6 to each student.

2. Explain that students are going to interview each other and draw a family tree based on the information they learn from their partner. Tell students they will each have 10 minutes to ask questions and draw their partner's family tree.

3. Have students first write the names of ten close family members on Activity Master 6 and then give the activity master to their partner.

4. Play the part of Student A. Call on an above-level student to play the part of Student B. Take Student B's activity master. Look at it and model the activity. Draw a box on the board.

   A: [Looks at Student B's activity master and writes Student B's name, *Sandra*, at the center of the box on the board. Then points to the first name on Sandra's list of family members and asks] *Who's Maria?*

   B: *She's my sister.*

   A: [Writes the name *Maria* on the board with a horizontal line to *Sandra* to indicate sisters.] *Who's Luis?*

   B: *He's my father.*

   A: [Writes the name *Luis* on the board with a vertical line to the other names to indicate father/child relationship.] For example:

   Luis
   |
   Maria — Sandra

5. Continue to model the activity asking about and adding other names from Sandra's list of family members to the family tree.

6. Have students tell their partners about their families. Each student will have a total of 10 minutes to explain his or her family relationships.

7. Circulate during the activity to help students ask clarifying questions when the family tree is unclear. For example: *Who is Van? Is he Trang's brother or cousin?*

8. Call out *time* at 10 minutes and have the partners switch roles.

Multilevel Options

Pre-level: During the activity, allow pre-level students to look at the family tree while it's being drawn so they can clarify family relationships and correct misunderstandings immediately.

Above-level: Tell above-level students not to show the family tree until the interview is completed and then show it to their partner to check their information.

Extension

After the class has finished the activity, have students look at their partner's family tree and write sentences about their partner's family on the board. For example:

Lucas has four brothers.

He also has two sisters.

Interview: *Tell me about your family.*

Part A. Complete this part with information about your family.

My name is _w_____.

These are the names of my family members:

_____   _____

_____   _____

_____   _____

_____   _____

_____   _____

Part B. Your partner draws your family tree here.

_____ 's Family Tree

Unit 2 • Lesson 6

Information Gap: *What do Patty and Sam have in common?*

Grouping Pairs
Target Language *have / live / work* simple present affirmative and negative, additions with *too / and . . . not / either*
Materials Activity Master 7
Class Time 20 minutes

Teacher Preparation

- Copy Activity Master 7, one for every two students.

- Cut each copy into two parts. Clip together Card A and Card B.

Procedure

1. Put students in like-ability pairs. Give a copy of Card A to Student A and a copy of Card B to Student B in each pair.

2. Hold up a copy of a card. Point to the Venn diagram. Explain that students are going to find out what Patty and Sam have and don't have in common and write the information in the correct areas.

3. Draw a large Venn diagram on the board. Play the part of Student A. Call on an above-level student to play the part of Student B. Then model the activity:

   A: *Tell me about Sam.*

   B: *Sam speaks English.*

   A: *Oh, really? Patty does, too.* [Writes *English* in the intersecting ovals.]

   B: *Sam also speaks French.*

   A: *Oh. Patty doesn't speak French but she speaks Chinese.* [Writes *Chinese* in Patty's oval and *French* in Sam's oval.] For example:

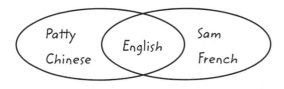

   Instruct all students to write the above language information in the Venn diagram on their cards.

4. To give students more support, write the model phrases on the board:

   He/she does, too.

   He/she doesn't, either.

5. Have pairs continue the activity. Tell students that they should take turns sharing information about the person on their cards.

6. Tell students not to show each other their cards.

7. Circulate during the activity to help students put the information in the correct part of the Venn diagram and to make sure they do not show their partners their cards until the end of the activity.

8. When pairs have shared all their information, have partners compare Venn diagrams to check their information. The information should be the same in both Venn diagrams.

Multilevel Option

Pre-level: During the activity, allow pre-level students to look at one another's Venn diagram so they can see what Patty and Sam have in common and correct misunderstandings immediately.

Extension

If some pairs finish before the rest of the class, have them write sentences about Patty and Sam. For example:

Patty speaks Chinese but Sam speaks French.

Patty doesn't have children and Sam doesn't either.

Information Gap: *What do Patty and Sam have in common?*

A: Patty

Languages: speaks English

speaks Chinese

Job: works in a school and
in a restaurant

Family: has one brother and no sisters

is not married

has no children

Home: lives in an apartment

lives in a big city

lives with brother and parents

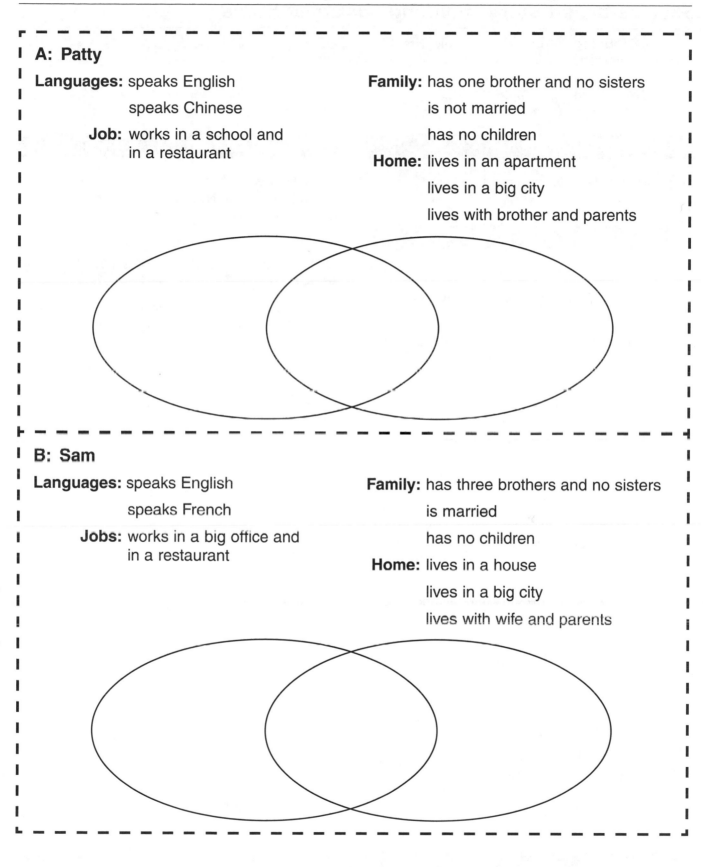

B: Sam

Languages: speaks English

speaks French

Jobs: works in a big office and
in a restaurant

Family: has three brothers and no sisters

is married

has no children

Home: lives in a house

lives in a big city

lives with wife and parents

Unit 2 • Lesson 7

Picture-based Story: *Sending Packages Home*

Grouping	Pairs and then whole class
Target Language	Mailing packages
Materials	Activity Master 8
Class Time	25 minutes

Teacher Preparation

Copy Activity Master 8, one for each student.

Procedure

1. Give a copy of Activity Master 8 to each student.

2. Explain that students are going to write a story based on the picture.

3. Put students in cross-ability pairs to discuss the questions on Activity Master 8.

4. Have students report their ideas to the class. Make sure students understand the scene: Eric lives in the United States. He's at the post office. He's sending gifts to his family and children back home.

5. Ask the class: *What's the story?* Have the class develop a story line orally.

6. Have students dictate the story line. Listen to students' ideas, repeat the ideas while rephrasing them in correct English, and write them on the board.

7. Have students copy the story into their notebooks.

Multilevel Option

Above-level: After they copy the story, have above-level students write comprehension questions about the story to ask the class.

Extension

- After the class has finished the activity, erase words from the story and have students tell you the missing words.

- Dictate a sentence from the story and have students write it down. Then write the sentence on the board so students can check their work. Repeat with other sentences.

Picture-based Story: *Sending Packages Home*

- Where is Eric?

- Who is he sending the packages to?

- What time of year is it?

- Does Eric live close to his family?

- How does he feel in this picture?

- What is Eric's family doing?

- Do they like the gifts?

- How do they feel in this picture?

1. **PAIRS: Discuss the questions under each picture.**

2. **CLASS: Tell the story to the teacher.**

Find Someone Who: *Do you have three sisters?*

Grouping Whole-class mixer
Target Language Family, simple present *yes / no* questions
Materials Activity Master 9
Class Time 20 minutes

Teacher Preparation

Copy Activity Master 9, one for each student.

Procedure

1. Give a copy of Activity Master 9 to each student.

2. Explain that students are going to walk around the classroom. They will ask and answer *yes / no* questions in order to complete as many sentences on Activity Master 9 as possible. Tell students they will have 15 minutes for the activity.

3. Write Do you _____ ? on the board. Have students complete the question for the first item, *Do you have three sisters?* You may want to point out that the verb changes in the question form. Then model the activity. Walk around the classroom, asking students *Do you have three sisters?* until you get a *yes* answer. Write the student's name to complete the first sentence on the board.

4. Circulate during the activity to help students formulate questions correctly.

Multilevel Option

Above-level: To increase the difficulty for above-level students, have them write three additional sentence prompts on the survey to extend the activity. For example:

_____ works long hours.

Extension

After the class has finished the activity, have students read aloud their sentences so the class can learn about people they didn't have a chance to talk to.

Variation

Have students do the activity in groups of 4. After 10 minutes, have students report to the class what they learned about their group members. The rest of the class listens and completes Activity Master 9.

Find Someone Who: *Do you have three sisters?*

Name	
	has three sisters.
	has two children.
	has more than 20 cousins.
	lives with a brother or sister.
	lives with a niece or a nephew.
	doesn't have a big family.
	doesn't live in an apartment.
	calls his or her family once a week.
	emails his or her family to keep in touch
	visits family on holidays.
	works in a hotel.
	works in a restaurant.
	doesn't work in a hospital.
	has two jobs.

Unit 2 • Review

Board Game: *Do you have family in this country?*

Grouping Groups of 4
Target Language Simple present affirmative and negative, simple present information and *yes / no* questions
Materials Activity Master 10, a coin, two markers for each group
Class Time 20 minutes

Teacher Preparation

Copy Activity Master 10, one for every four students.

Procedure

1. Put students in like-ability pairs. Each pair is a team. Put two teams together to play the game. Give each group of 4 a copy of Activity Master 10, a coin, and two markers.

2. Explain that students are going to play a board game. Here are the rules:

   - Pair 1 flips a coin to move. *Heads* means the team moves the marker ahead two squares and *tails* means the team moves their marker ahead one square.

   - Pair 1 moves the marker to a square. Student A forms the question. Student B answers the question and adds one more sentence. For example:

     A: *Do you have any sisters?*

     B: *Yes, I do. I have two sisters.*

   - Pair 2 listens to make sure Pair 1's question and answer are correct.

   - If Pair 1's question and answer are correct, Pair 2 takes a turn.

   - If Pair 1's question and answer are incorrect, Pair 1 moves the marker back one square, and Pair 2 takes a turn.

   - If a pair lands on a square that already has a marker on it, the pair gets to move forward one square.

   - The first pair to reach FINISH wins.

3. Circulate during the activity to make sure students' answers are correct.

Extension

If some groups finish before the rest of the class, have each student write three true sentences about their partner. For example:

Ahn lives with her family.

She has two nieces.

She has two jobs.

Answer Key

1. Do you have family in this country?
2. Do you have any sisters?
3. When do you visit your family?
4. Do you have a lot in common with your parents?
5. Do you live with your mother-in-law?
6. How many nieces and nephews do you have?
7. How do you keep in touch with your family?
8. Where do you work?
9. Where does your family live?
10. How often do you e-mail your family?
11. Do you live in an apartment?
12. Do you have two jobs?
13. Do you work on the weekends?
14. How often do you call your family?

Board Game: *Do you have family in this country?*

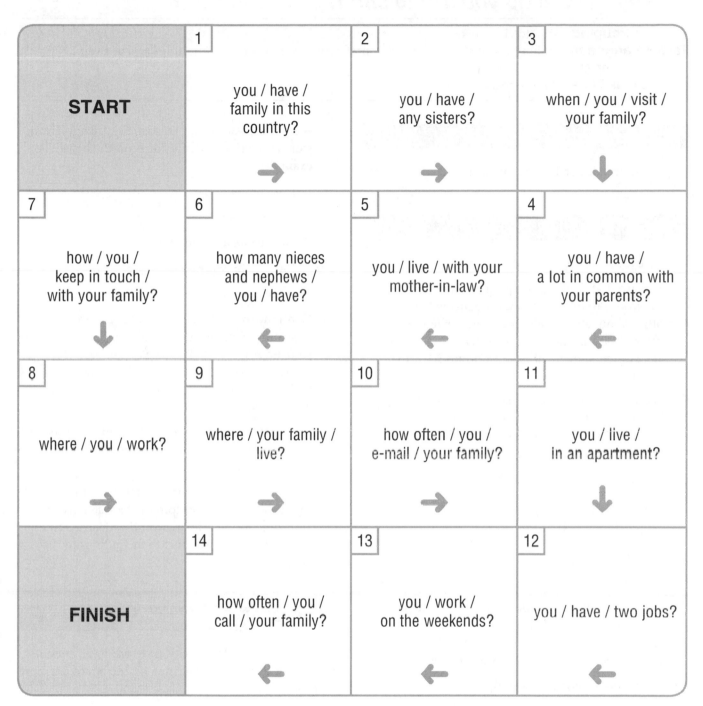

	1 you / have / family in this country? →	**2** you / have / any sisters? →	**3** when / you / visit / your family? ↓
START			
7 how / you / keep in touch / with your family? ↓	**6** how many nieces and nephews / you / have? ←	**5** you / live / with your mother-in-law? ←	**4** you / have / a lot in common with your parents? ←
8 where / you / work? →	**9** where / your family / live? →	**10** how often / you / e-mail / your family? →	**11** you / live / in an apartment? ↓
FINISH	**14** how often / you / call / your family? ←	**13** you / work / on the weekends? ←	**12** you / have / two jobs? ←

Unit 3 • Lesson 3

Survey: *Where do you like to shop?*

Grouping	Whole-class mixer
Target Language	Talking about stores, expressing preferences, simple present questions and answers
Materials	Activity Master 11
Class Time	20 minutes

Teacher Preparation

Copy Activity Master 11, one for each student.

Procedure

1. Give a copy of Activity Master 11 to each student.

2. Explain that students are going to walk around the classroom to take a survey. Students will ask each other about store preferences and write the information in the chart on Activity Master 11. Tell students they will have 15 minutes for the activity.

3. Write on the board the question *Where do you like to shop for _____?* Ask students to brainstorm different items to shop for. Write their ideas on the board. For example:

   shoes

   coats

   food

   phones

   children's clothes

   Tell each student to choose a shopping category from the board and complete the question on Activity Master 11. Encourage students to choose different shopping categories to investigate.

4. Model the activity. For example:

   A: *Where do you like to shop for shoes?*

   B: *I like to go to Lipton's for shoes.*

   A: *Why?*

   B: *Because it has good prices.*

   Write Student B's answer on your activity master.

5. Ask the class for other reasons they like a certain store and write students' ideas on the board. For example:

   It has good prices.

   It's convenient.

   The people are friendly.

   It's easy to return and exchange things.

   It has a lot of different kinds of _____.

6. Continue to model the activity. Walk around the classroom. Stop at the desk of another above-level student. Ask him or her to play the part of Student B. Ask, *Where do you like to shop for shoes?* and *Why?* Write Student B's answers on your activity master.

7. Circulate during the activity to help students ask and answer the two questions. Students may need help explaining why they like the store.

8. At the end of the activity ask students to complete the sentence at the bottom of their activity master according to the information they learned in the survey. Have them report their findings to the class.

Multilevel Options

Pre-level: During the activity, have pre-level students refer to the explanations written on the board for more language support.

Above-level: Tell above-level students to do the activity without looking at the explanations written on the board.

Survey: *Where do you like to shop?*

Where do you like to shop for _____?	Why?

The student's favorite store for _____ is _____

because _____.

Unit 3 • Lesson 6

Future 2 pages 56–57

Information Gap: *What are Marta's plans for Saturday?*

Grouping	Pairs
Target Language	*Be going to*, talking about plans and errands
Materials	Activity Master 12
Class Time	20 minutes

Teacher Preparation

• Copy Activity Master 12, one for every two students.

• Cut each copy into two parts. Clip together Schedule A and Schedule B.

Procedure

1. Put students in like-ability pairs. Give a copy of Schedule A to Student A and a copy of Schedule B to Student B in each pair.

2. Hold up a copy Schedule A. Explain that students are going to fill in the missing information in their schedules by asking each other about Marta's plans.

3. Play the part of Student A. Call on an above-level student to play the part of Student B. Then model the activity:

   A: *What are Marta's plans for Saturday? What is she going to do in the morning?*

   B: *First she's going to cash her check at the bank.*

   A: *She's going to cash her check at the bank?* [Writes down information.]

   Instruct all Student As to write *cash check* on the first line of their schedules.

4. Have pairs continue the activity.

5. Tell students not to show each other their schedules.

6. Circulate during the activity to help students with spelling and to make sure they do not show their partners their schedules until the end of the activity.

7. After pairs have filled in their schedules, have partners compare cards to check their information. The information on both cards should be the same.

Multilevel Options

Pre-level: Encourage pre-level students to refer to the question and response box on their schedule cards for guidance during the conversations.

Above-level: Have above-level students fold the question and response box under the schedule and form the questions and responses on their own.

Extension

If some pairs finish before the rest of the class, have them write about Marta's day in sentences. For example:

> In the morning Marta is going to cash her check at the bank. Then she's going to mail a package and buy stamps at the post office.

Information Gap: *What are Marta's plans for Saturday?*

	Schedule A—*Saturday, June 2*
morning	bank—_____ post office—_____ bakery—_____ drugstore—_____
afternoon	library—return books Lacy's Department Store—exchange jeans grocery store—get groceries laundromat—pick up wool pants
evening	5:30—_____ 6:00—go out to dinner at Best Seafood with Lisa and Kate 8:00—_____

Ask questions about Schedule B:
What is she going to do in the morning?
And then what is she going to do?
What is she going to do at *5:30*?

Answer questions about Schedule B:
First she's going to

_____ at

the _____ .

Then she's going to

_____ at

the _____ .

At 6:00 she's going to

_____ .

	Schedule B—*Saturday, June 2*
morning	bank—cash check post office—mail package and buy stamps bakery—get bread drugstore—pick up medicine
afternoon	library—_____ Lacy's Department Store—_____ grocery store—_____ laundromat—_____
evening	5:30—pick up Lisa and Kate 6:00—_____ 8:00—meet Joe at Central Movie Theater

Ask questions about Schedule A:
What is Marta going to do in the *afternoon*?
What is Marta going to do at *6:00*?

Answer questions about Schedule A:
First she's going to

_____ at

the _____ .

Then she's going to

_____ at

the _____ .

At 5:30 she's going to

_____ .

Picture-based Story: *A Big Purchase*

Grouping	Pairs and then whole class
Target Language	Paying bills, using credit cards
Materials	Activity Master 13
Class Time	25 minutes

Teacher Preparation

Copy Activity Master 13, one for each student.

Procedure

1. Give a copy of Activity Master 13 to each student.

2. Explain that students are going to write a story based on the pictures.

3. Put students in cross-ability pairs to discuss the questions on Activity Master 13.

4. Have students report their ideas to the class. Make sure students understand the scenes:

    (1) Abby's refrigerator is broken. Abby needs to get a new one. She sees an ad in the newspaper for a refrigerator on clearance for $698 at the T-Store.

    (2) At the store, the salesman shows her a bigger and more expensive refrigerator. With a store credit card she can get a 10% discount.

    (3) She decides to buy the bigger refrigerator with her store credit card. She is happy.

    (4) Six months later she is having a hard time paying the credit card bill for the new refrigerator.

5. Ask the class: *What's the story?* Have the class develop a story line orally. Write key vocabulary words on the board.

6. Have students return to working in pairs to write a draft of their story. Circulate around the classroom, helping students with their writing.

7. As students finish their stories, put them together with another pair to share their stories and give one another feedback.

8. Have students write a final copy of their story to submit to you for your corrections and feedback.

Multilevel Option

Above-level: After they copy the story, have above-level students write comprehension questions about the story to ask the class.

Extension

- Ask students: *What can Abby do to pay her credit card bill?* Write their ideas on the board. Have students copy the solutions down and circle the one they think is best. Have them discuss their reasons with the class.

- Have students write the conversation between the salesman and Abby in the store.

Picture-based Story: *A Big Purchase*

• What's the problem?

• Which refrigerator does she buy? Why?

• How does she feel about her purchase?

• How does she feel about her purchase six months later? Why?

• What happens next?

1. **PAIRS: Discuss the questions under each picture.**

2. **CLASS: Tell the story to the teacher. Write down the new vocabulary.**

3. **PAIRS: Write your story together.**

Match the Sentences: *All About Clothes*

Grouping	Pairs
Target Language	Simple present with *need, want* + infinitive, adverbs of degree *too* and *very*, clothes and their materials
Materials	Activity Master 14
Class Time	20 minutes

Teacher Preparation

- Copy Activity Master 14, one for each pair of students.

- Cut each copy into 20 cards. The white cards are the first sentences and the gray cards are the second sentences.

  Note: You may want to start with only the first five pairs.

- Clip each set of cards together.

Procedure

1. Put students in like-ability pairs. Give a set of cards to each pair.

2. Tell Student A to shuffle the white cards and Student B to shuffle the gray cards. Have students put their cards face up on their desks.

3. Explain that students are going to work together to connect pairs of sentences in a logical way. Tell students that the white cards are the first sentences and the gray cards are the second sentences.

4. Model the activity. Assemble the first white card (number 1) and the gray card into a correct sentence and read it aloud: *I need a size small blouse. It's too loose.*

5. Write the two sentences on the board. Tell students to assemble the sentences with their cards.

6. Tell students to continue to assemble correct sentences.

7. Circulate during the activity to make sure students' matched sentences are correct.

Multilevel Option

Pre-level: Give pre-level students only the first ten cards so that they have fewer choices to consider as they match the cards. When they finish the first half of the cards, give them the second half.

Variation

Mixer: Use one copy of Activity Master 14. Give each student a card at random. Have students walk around the classroom. They continually say their sentence until they find the connecting sentence. If there are more than 20 students, use two copies of Activity Master 14.

Match the Sentences: *All About Clothes*

1. I need a size small blouse.	It's too loose.
2. I need a size large sweatshirt.	It's too tight.
3. I want to exchange these jeans.	They're too short.
4. I want to return these boots.	There's a hole in the leather.
5. I need to exchange this scarf.	The silk is ripped.
6. I can't buy that skirt.	It's too expensive.
7. I want to buy those shoes.	The price is very good.
8. I want to buy this dress.	It's very pretty.
9. I need to buy a wool coat.	It's too cold for a windbreaker.
10. I need to buy some shorts.	It's too hot for corduroy pants.

Unit 3 • Review

Board Game: *What are you going to do next week?*

Grouping	Groups of 4
Target Language	*Want* and *need*; *be going to*; talking about plans, clothing, and shopping
Materials	Activity Master 15, a coin, two markers for each group
Class Time	20 minutes

Teacher Preparation

Copy Activity Master 15, one for every four students.

Procedure

1. Put students in like-ability pairs. Each pair is a team. Put two teams together to play the game. Give each group of 4 a copy of Activity Master 15, a coin, and two markers.

2. Explain that students are going to play a board game. Here are the rules:

   • Pair 1 flips a coin to move. *Heads* means the team moves the marker ahead two squares and *tails* means the team moves their marker ahead one square.

   • Pair 1 moves the marker to a square. Student A reads the question aloud. Student B answers with true information. Pair 2 listens to make sure Pair 1's answer is correct.

   • If Pair 1's answer is correct, Pair 2 takes a turn.

   • If Pair 1's answer is incorrect, Pair 1 moves the marker back one square, and Pair 2 takes a turn.

   • If a pair lands on a square that already has a marker on it, the pair gets to move forward one square.

   • The first pair to reach FINISH wins.

3. Circulate during the activity to make sure students' answers are correct.

Extension

If some groups finish before the rest of the class, have each student write three true sentences about their partner. For example:

> Lee is going to go to work next week.
>
> He likes to shop for jeans at JJ Percy.
>
> He is wearing blue jeans, a wool sweater, and boots.

Board Game: *What are you going to do next week?*

START	**1** What are you going to do next week? →	**2** Where do you like to shop for jeans? →	**3** What is a good reason to return a jacket? ↓
7 What do you want to do next summer? ↓	**6** Where do you like to shop for shoes? ←	**5** What errands do you need to run tomorrow? ←	**4** What is your partner wearing? ←
8 What do you want to do next weekend? →	**9** What clothes do you wear in the summer? →	**10** What is a good reason to exchange a shirt? →	**11** What are you wearing? ↓
FINISH	**14** What do you need to buy soon? Why? ←	**13** What are your plans for tonight? ←	**12** Do you like to pay for things in cash? Why? Why not? ←

Unit 4 • Lesson 3

Survey: *Free-time Activities*

Grouping Whole-class mixer
Target Language Free-time activities, questions with *how often*, frequency expressions
Materials Activity Master 16
Class Time 20 minutes

Teacher Preparation

Copy Activity Master 16, one for each student.

Procedure

1. Give a copy of Activity Master 16 to each student.

2. Explain that students are going to walk around the classroom to take a survey. Students will ask each other questions and record the responses in the chart on Activity Master 16. Tell students they will have 15 minutes for the activity.

3. Have students look through the list of activities and check five they want to ask about. Then have them write the five activities into the question column of their chart. Chose several activities for your own activity master, too. For example:

How often do you ...	Every day	A few times a week	Once a week	Once a month	Never
study English?					
read the newspaper in English?					
watch TV in English?					

4. Play the part of Student A. Call on an above-level student to play the part of Student B. Then model the activity:

    A: *How often do you study English?*

    B: *Every day.*

    Record Student B's response to your question by checking the appropriate column on your activity master. Show the class where you wrote the check on your activity master.

5. Continue to model the activity:

    A: *How often do you read the newspaper in English?*

    B: *Never.*

    Record Student B's response to your second question by checking the appropriate column on your activity master.

6. Continue to ask Student B the remaining questions on your activity master and record the answers in the chart.

7. Circulate during the activity to help students ask and answer their five questions.

Multilevel Option

Above-level: Tell above-level students to do the activity without looking at the word box.

Extension

After the class has finished the activity, have students tally their results and draw a bar graph for each question with the information they gathered from their classmates. For example:

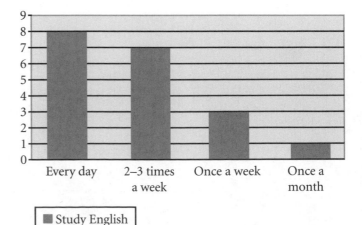

□ Study English

Survey: *Free-time Activities*

How often do you . . .	Every day	A few times a week	Once a week	Once a month	Never

Free-time activities

do your homework	go out to eat	play soccer
exercise	go shopping	read the newspaper in English
go dancing	go to the beach	rent DVDs
go fishing	go to the movies	stay home on Saturday night
go for a bike ride	go to the park	study English
go for a walk	have dinner with friends	watch English TV
go hiking	listen to English music	watch TV programs from your country
go jogging	play on the computer	

Unit 4 • Lesson 6

Find Someone Who: *Likes and Dislikes*

Grouping   Whole-class mixer
Target Language   Free-time activities, expressing likes and dislikes, simple present *yes / no* questions
Materials   Activity Master 17
Class Time   20 minutes

Teacher Preparation

Copy Activity Master 17, one for each student.

Procedure

1. Give a copy of Activity Master 17 to each student.

2. Explain that students are going to walk around the classroom. They will ask and answer *Do you like to _____?* in order to complete as many sentences on Activity Master 17 as possible. Tell students they will have 15 minutes for the activity.

3. Write the model responses to the *yes / no* question on the board:

   Yes, I do. I love to _____.

   Yes, I do. I like to _____.

   No, I don't. I don't like to _____.

   No, I don't. I hate to _____.

4. Write *Do you like to _____?* on the board. Fill in the blank with the first item, *go jogging*. Then model the activity. Walk around the classroom, asking students *Do you like to go jogging?* until you get a *Yes, I do* answer. Write the student's name to complete the first sentence on the activity master.

5. Circulate during the activity to help students respond to the questions correctly.

Multilevel Option

Above-level: To increase the difficulty for above-level students, have them write three additional sentence prompts on the survey to extend the activity. For example:

_____ loves to go swimming.

_____ hates to eat out.

_____ likes to vacuum.

Extension

After the class has finished the activity, have students read their sentences aloud so the class can learn about people they didn't have a chance to talk to.

Variation

Have students do the activity in groups of 4. After 5 minutes, have students report to the class what they learned about their group members. The rest of the class listens and completes Activity Master 17.

Find Someone Who: *Likes and Dislikes*

Name	
	likes to go jogging.
	loves to go clothes shopping.
	doesn't like to play on the computer.
	likes to wash the dishes.
	hates to iron clothes.
	loves to go dancing.
	doesn't like to go to loud parties.
	loves to go grocery shopping.
	likes to exercise.
	doesn't like to cook.
	hates to get up early.
	doesn't like to go to the movies.
	loves to read.
	doesn't like to watch TV.
	hates to clean the house.

Picture-based Story: *An Evening Out*

Grouping Pairs and then whole class
Target Language Rude and polite behavior
Materials Activity Master 18
Class Time 25 minutes

Teacher Preparation

Copy Activity Master 18, one for each student.

Procedure

1. Give a copy of Activity Master 18 to each student.

2. Explain that students are going to write a story based on the pictures.

3. Put students in cross-ability pairs to discuss the questions on Activity Master 18.

4. Have students report their ideas to the class. Make sure students understand the scenes:

   (1) Anna and Yoshi are at a nice restaurant.

   (2) Yoshi is slurping his soup. Anna is surprised. She thinks he is very rude.

   (3) Yoshi is telling Anna that in his country everyone slurps their soup. It shows they like the food.

5. Ask the class: *What's the story?* Have the class develop a <u>general</u> story line orally. Write key vocabulary words on the board.

6. Have students return to working in pairs to write a draft of their story. Circulate around the classroom helping students with their writing.

7. As students finish their stories, put them together with another pair to share their stories and give one another feedback.

8. Have students write a final copy of their story to submit to you for your corrections and feedback.

Multilevel Option

Above-level: Have above-level students be the scribes in their pairs.

Extension

Have students role-play the conversation between Yoshi and Anna.

Picture-based Story: *An Evening Out*

• Where are Anna and Yoshi?

• What are they going to eat?

• What is Anna thinking?

• What is Yoshi thinking?

• What is Yoshi telling Anna?

1. **PAIRS: Discuss the questions under each picture.**

2. **CLASS: Tell the story to the teacher. Write down the new vocabulary.**

3. **PAIRS: Write your story together.**

Mix and Match: *Conversations*

Grouping Pairs
Target Language Talk about weekend activities, likes and dislikes; invite someone to do something; accept an invitation
Materials Activity Master 19
Class Time 20 minutes

Teacher Preparation

- Copy Activity Master 19, one for each pair of students.

- Cut each copy into 13 cards. The white cards are Speaker A and the gray cards are Speaker B.

- Clip each set of cards together.

Procedure

1. Put students in like-ability pairs. Give a set of cards to each pair.

2. Tell Student A to shuffle the white cards and Student B to shuffle the gray cards. Have each student put their cards face up on their desks.

3. Explain that students are going to work together to make three different dialogues with the cards. Tell students that Speaker A always begins the conversation (white cards).

4. Model the activity. Pull out a Speaker A card with a question, for example: *Do you want to go out for coffee?* Ask the class to look for the response in the B cards (gray cards). When a student finds it, have the student call it out so everyone can find it. *Sorry. I can't. I have to study right now. How about a little later?*

5. Tell students to continue in pairs to find the response to Speaker A's response.

6. Circulate during the activity to make sure students' matched dialogues are correct.

Multilevel Option

Pre-level: Identify the first card in each of the three conversations to scaffold the activity for pre-level students.

Extension

If some pairs complete the activity before the rest of the class, have partners take turns picking up card with a question on it. The other partner responds in his or her own words.

Mix and Match: *Conversations*

A: What are you doing this Saturday?	B: I'm going to go to the zoo with my family.
A: Really? How often do you go there?	B: About once a month. What about you? What are you doing?
A: I'm going to go to the beach with some friends.	B: That sounds like fun.
A: What do you like to do on the weekends?	B: I like to clean my house.
A: You're kidding.	B: No, really. I find it relaxing.
A: Do you want to go out for coffee?	B: Sorry. I can't. I have to study right now. How about a little later?
A: Sure. Sounds great.	

Unit 4 • Review

Board Game: *Free-time Activities*

Grouping Groups of 4
Target Language Talking about likes and dislikes and free-time activities, simple present, adverbs of frequency
Materials Activity Master 20, a coin, two markers for each group
Class Time 20 minutes

Teacher Preparation

Copy Activity Master 20, one for every four students.

Procedure

1. Put students in like-ability pairs. Each pair is a team. Put two teams together to play the game. Give each group of 4 a copy of Activity Master 20, a coin, and two markers.

2. Explain that students are going to play a board game. Here are the rules:

   • Pair 1 flips a coin to move. *Heads* means the team moves the marker ahead two squares and *tails* means the team moves their marker ahead one square.

   • Pair 1 moves the marker to a square. Student A forms the question. Student B answers with true information. Pair 2 listens to make sure Pair 1's question and answer are correct.

   • If Pair 1's question and answer are correct, Pair 2 takes a turn.

   • If Pair 1's question and answer are incorrect, Pair 1 moves the marker back one square, and Pair 2 takes a turn.

   • If a pair lands on a square that already has a marker on it, the pair gets to move forward one square.

   • The first pair to reach FINISH wins.

3. Circulate during the activity to make sure students' answers are correct.

Extension

If some groups finish before the rest of the class, have each student write three true sentences about his or her partner. For example:

Sonia is going to clean the house this Saturday.

Sonia doesn't like to go dancing.

Sonia hates to go to loud parties.

Answer Key

1. How often do you go out to eat?
2. Do you like to go dancing?
3. What are you doing this Saturday?
4. How often do you exercise?
5. How often do you iron clothes?
6. What do you do in your free time?
7. Do you want to take a walk?
8. What are you doing this Sunday?
9. How often do you do your homework?
10. Do you like to go fishing?
11. What do you hate to do?
12. Do you want to go for a bike ride?
13. When does this class meet?
14. How often do you go to the movies?

Board Game: *Free-time Activities*

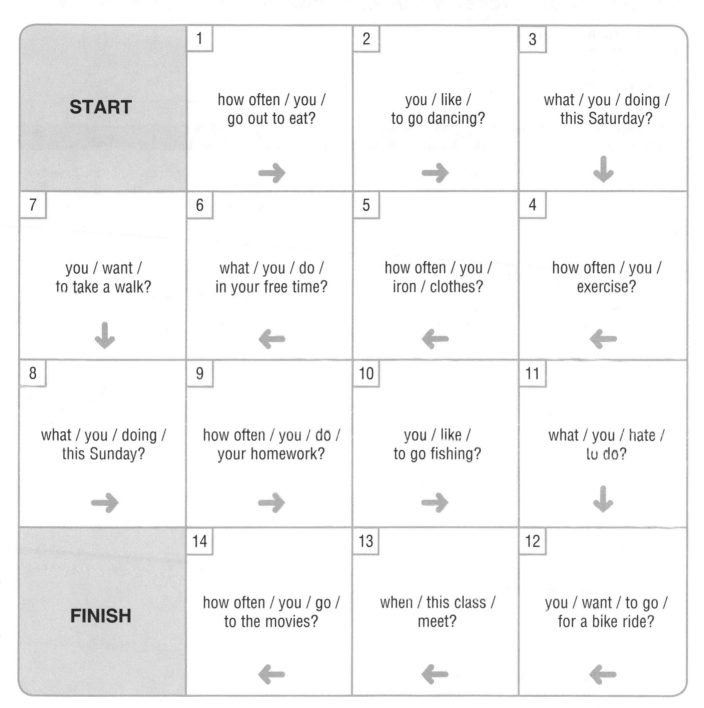

START	1 how often / you / go out to eat? →	2 you / like / to go dancing? →	3 what / you / doing / this Saturday? ↓
7 you / want / to take a walk? ↓	6 what / you / do / in your free time? ←	5 how often / you / iron / clothes? ←	4 how often / you / exercise? ←
8 what / you / doing / this Sunday? →	9 how often / you / do / your homework? →	10 you / like / to go fishing? →	11 what / you / hate / to do? ↓
FINISH	14 how often / you / go / to the movies? ←	13 when / this class / meet? ←	12 you / want / to go / for a bike ride? ←

Unit 5 • Lesson 3

Information Gap: *Today at 101 Broadway*

Grouping	Pairs
Target Language	Describing problems in the home, present continuous
Materials	Activity Master 21
Class Time	20 minutes

Teacher Preparation

• Copy Activity Master 21, one for every two students.

• Cut each copy into two parts. Clip together Card A and Card B.

Procedure

1. Put students in like-ability groups. Give a copy of Card A to Student A and a copy of Card B to Student B in each pair.

2. Explain that students are going to find out what is happening today at 101 Broadway.

3. Play the part of Student A. Call on above-level students to play the part of Student B. Then model the activity:

    A: *What's the problem in Apartment 1C?*

    B: *The bedroom window is stuck.*

    A: *The bedroom window is stuck?*

    B: *Yes.*

    Instruct all Student As to write *is stuck* after *The bedroom window* on the line in Apt 1C on their card. (*The bedroom window is stuck.*)

4. Have groups continue the activity. Tell students that they should not show each other their cards.

5. Circulate during the activity to help students clarify the information and to make sure they do not show their group members their cards until the end of the activity.

6. When the group members have shared all their information, have them compare their cards to check their information. All the information from Cards A and B should be the same.

Multilevel Option

Above-level: Make a copy of Activity Master 21 and block out more information from the cards so that the above-level students have to write complete sentences and not just phrases when they do the activity. For example:

Apt. 1A	Apt. 1B	Apt. 1C
_____	The locks are	_____
_____	broken on the	_____
_____	front door	_____
_____	_____.	_____

Extension

If some pairs finish before the rest of the class, have them write three sentences beginning with the following:

The building manager should _____.

Information Gap: *Today at 101 Broadway*

Card A

Apt. 2A The shower _____.	Apt. 2B The kitchen sink is clogged.	Apt. 2C The lights _____ _____.
Apt. 1A The bathroom ceiling _____ _____.	Apt. 1B The locks on the front door are broken.	Apt. 1C The bedroom window _____.
Building Office The building manager is talking on the phone.	Utility Room The radiator _____.	Laundry Room Two washing machines are out of order.

- -

Card B

Apt. 2A The shower is broken.	Apt. 2B The kitchen sink _____ _____.	Apt. 2C The lights aren't working.
Apt. 1A The bathroom ceiling is leaking.	Apt. 1B The locks on the front door _____.	Apt. 1C The bedroom window is stuck.
Building Office The building manager is _____.	Utility Room The radiator isn't working.	Laundry Room Two washing machines _____.

Unit 5 • Lesson 6

Rental Apartment Match: *How many bedrooms are there?*

Grouping	Whole-class mixer
Target Language	Questions with , , apartment ads, asking about an apartment
Materials	Activity Master 22
Class Time	20 minutes

Teacher Preparation

• Copy Activity Master 22. Make two copies.

• Cut each copy into 12 cards (total of 24 cards).

Procedure

1. Give one card to each student at random. If there are fewer than 24 students, make sure to have duplicate cards of the same apartment. Have students read the ad for a rental apartment on the card silently.

2. Explain that students are going to walk around the classroom. They will ask and answer questions in order to find a matching card. Tell students not to show their cards to anyone. They will have 15 minutes for the activity.

3. Brainstorm with the class the kinds of questions they need to ask about the rental apartment on their card. Write the following questions on the board:

   How many <u>bedrooms</u> are there? (bathrooms)

   Is there a <u>living room</u>? (dining room / parking garage / washer and dryer)

   Is there a <u>bus stop</u> nearby? (park / supermarket / school)

   Are there a lot of <u>closets</u>? (windows)

   Are pets allowed?

   How much is the rent?

   Are utilities included?

4. Play the part of Student A. Look at your card. Walk around the classroom. Ask an above-level student to play the part of Student B. Ask the questions on the board until you find your cards have a difference. For example:

A: *How many bedrooms are there?*

B: *There are three.*

A: *OK. My apartment has three bedrooms, too. How many bathrooms are there?*

B: *There is one.*

A: *Oh, my apartment has two bathrooms.*

Continue to call on above-level students until you get a match.

Note: Remind students that they should continue to question students until they find a match.

5. Circulate during the activity to make sure students are not showing anyone their cards and are forming correct sentences.

6. When students find a match, give each another card to continue the activity.

Multilevel Options

Pre-level: During the activity, allow pre-level students to refer to the questions on the board.

Above-level: Tell above-level students to do the activity without looking at the questions on the board.

Extension

After students have found their match and you are running out of extra cards, have them sit down together and write their advertisement in complete sentences. For example:

There are three-bedrooms and two bathrooms. There is an eat-in-kitchen.

Rental Apartment Match: *How many bedrooms are there?*

Large 3 BR, 2 BA, LR, EIK. W/D in basement. Pkg. garage. Nr. bus stop, park, school. Pets ok. $1,400/mo. Utilities not incl.	Large 3 BR, 1 BA, LR, EIK. W/D in basement. Lots of closets. Nr. bus stop, park, school. Pets ok. $1,400/mo. Utilities not incl.
Large 3 BR, 1 BA, LR, EIK. W/D in basement. Lots of windows. Pkg. garage. Nr. bus stop, park, school. No pets. $1,400/mo. Utilities not incl.	Large 3 BR, 2 BA, LR, EIK. Lots of closets Pkg. garage. Nr. bus stop, park, school. Pets ok. $1,400/mo. Utilities not incl.
Large 3 BR, 2 BA, LR, EIK. W/D in basement. Pkg. garage. Nr. bus stop & supermarket. Pets ok. $1,400/mo. Utilities not incl.	Large 3 BR, 2 BA, LR, EIK. W/D in basement. Pkg. garage. Nr. bus stop, park, school. Pets ok. $1,200/mo. Utilities not incl.
Large 3 BR, 2 BA, LR, EIK. W/D in basement. Pkg. garage. Nr. bus stop & supermarket. Pets ok. $1,400/mo. Utilities incl.	Large 3 BR, 2 BA, EIK. W/D in basement. Pkg. garage. Nr. bus stop & supermarket. No pets. $1,400/mo. Utilities not incl.
Large 3 BR, 2 BA, LR, EIK. W/D in basement. Pkg. garage. Nr. bus stop, park, school. No pets. $1,400/mo. Utilities not incl.	Large 3 BR, 2 BA, LR, EIK. W/D in basement. Pkg. garage. Nr. bus stop, park, school. Pets ok. $1,400/mo. Utilities incl.
Large 3 BR, 1 BA, EIK. W/D in basement. Pkg. garage. Nr. bus stop, park, school. Pets ok. $1,400/mo. Utilities not incl.	Large 3 BR, 1 BA, LR, EIK. W/D in basement. Pkg. garage. Nr. bus stop & school. Pets ok. $1,200/mo. Utilities incl.

Unit 5 • Lesson 7

Future 2 pages 98–99

Picture-based Story: *Moving On*

Grouping	Pairs and then the whole class
Target Language	Present continuous, describing different communities
Materials	Activity Master 23
Class Time	25 minutes

Teacher Preparation

Copy Activity Master 23, one for each student.

Procedure

1. Give a copy of Activity Master 23 to each student.

2. Explain that students are going to write a story based on the pictures.

3. Put students in cross-ability pairs to discuss the questions about the pictures on Activity Master 23.

4. Have students report their ideas to the class. Make sure students understand the scenes:

   (1) Marta is talking to her sister. Her sister lives in a house. The weather is warm and sunny. Marta and her family are living in an apartment in a crowded, dirty, and polluted neighborhood. The weather is cold.

   (2) Marta and Tomas are moving from their apartment in the city. They are happy. They're going to have a big house and a nice yard. It's going to be warm and clean.

   (3) They are arriving to their new town. They're not happy. It is crowded, dirty, and polluted— just like their old neighborhood a thousand miles away.

5. Ask the class: *What's the story?* Have students describe each picture. Write key vocabulary words on the board.

6. Have students return to working in pairs to write a draft of their story. Circulate around the classroom, helping students with their writing.

7. As students finish their stories, put them together with another pair to share their stories and give one another feedback.

8. Have students write a final copy of their story to submit to you for your corrections and feedback.

Multilevel Option

Above-level: Have above-level students be the scribes in their pairs.

Extension

Have students cut out the pictures, making a three-page story with a picture and text on each page. Have them share their books with the class.

Picture-based Story: *Moving On*

- What is Marta talking to her sister about?
- What is Marta's neighborhood like?
- What is the weather like?

- What are Marta and Tomas doing?
- Why are they leaving?
- Where are they moving to?

- What is their new neighborhood like?
- How are Tomas and Marta feeling now?
- What happens next?

1. **PAIRS: Discuss the questions under each picture.**

2. **CLASS: Tell the story to the teacher. Write down the new vocabulary.**

3. **PAIRS: Write your story together.**

Unit 5 • Lesson 8

Question and Answer Game: *Can you give me directions?*

Grouping	Pairs
Target Language	Giving directions
Materials	Activity Master 24
Class Time	20 minutes

Teacher Preparation

- Copy Activity Master 24, one for each pair.
- Cut each activity master into 13 parts—the map and 12 cards. Clip each set together.

Procedure

1. Put students in like-ability pairs. Give a map and a set of cards to each pair.

2. Explain that students are going to ask for and give directions. They will use the map to give each other directions to destinations written on the cards. They will have 15 minutes to do the activity.

3. Have students look at the map and identify the names of the businesses and the streets. Also have them locate the phrase "You are here" on the map.

4. Model the activity. Play the part of Student A. Choose an above-level student to play the role of Student B. For example:

   A: [Picks a card that says *Metro Bank.*] *Can you give me directions to Metro Bank?*

   B: *Sure. Go straight on Maple Avenue. Turn right on Main Street. Go straight. Go through the traffic light. At the stop sign, turn right. Metro Bank is on your right.*

   A: [Follows the directions on the map with a finger.] *Thanks.*

5. Circulate during the activity to clarify directions and correct pronunciation.

Multilevel Option

Pre-level: Instead of taking turns to ask for and give directions, have pre-level pairs work together to create directions to different places on the map.

Variation

Have students work in groups of 3. Have students select four destination cards and then write directions to those places on the map. In small groups, have students read their directions aloud without giving the name of the destination. The group members must listen to the directions and identify the destination.

Extension

Have pairs choose a different starting point and then continue the activity by asking for and giving directions from that point to other places on the map.

Question and Answer Game: *Can you give me directions?*

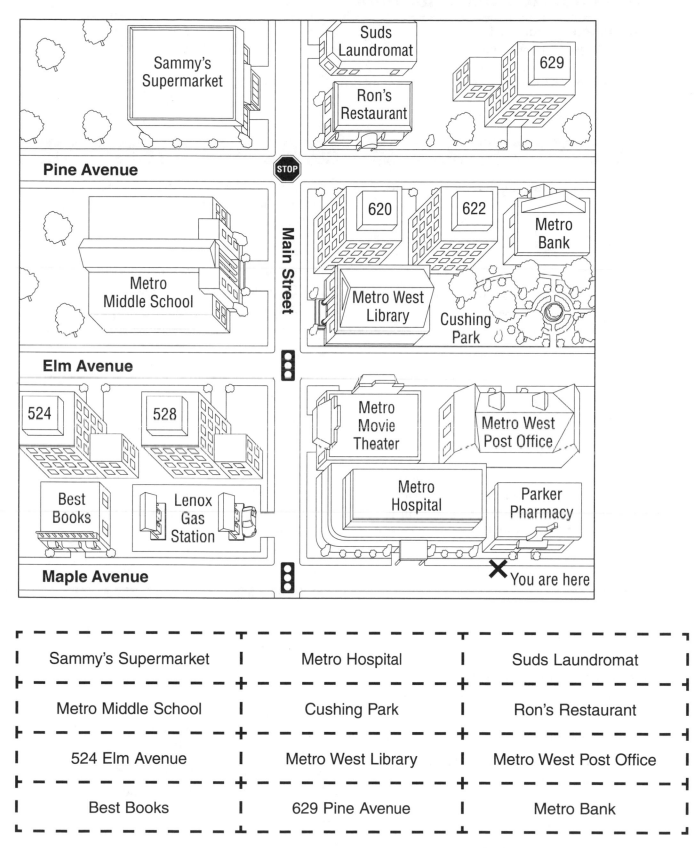

Sammy's Supermarket	Metro Hospital	Suds Laundromat
Metro Middle School	Cushing Park	Ron's Restaurant
524 Elm Avenue	Metro West Library	Metro West Post Office
Best Books	629 Pine Avenue	Metro Bank

Unit 5 • Review

Board Game: *Apartment for Rent*

Grouping	Groups of 4
Target Language	Asking about an apartment, read an apartment ad, getting and giving directions, questions with *there*, affirmative and negative short answers with *be*
Materials	Activity Master 25, a coin, two markers for each group
Class Time	20 minutes

Teacher Preparation

Copy Activity Master 25, one for every four students.

Procedure

1. Put students in like-ability pairs. Each pair is a team. Put two teams together to play the game. Give each group of 4 a copy of Activity Master 25, a coin, and two markers.

2. Explain that students are going to play a board game. Here are the rules:

   • Pair 1 flips a coin to move. *Heads* means the team moves the marker ahead two squares and *tails* means the team moves their marker ahead one square.

   • Pair 1 moves the marker to a square. Student A forms the question. Student B answers with information from the apartment ad and map. Pair B listens to make sure Pair 1's question and answer are correct.

   • If Pair 1's question and answer are correct, Pair 2 takes a turn.

   • If Pair 1's question and answer are incorrect, Pair 1 moves the marker back one square, and Pair 1 takes a turn.

   • If a pair lands on a square that already has a marker on it, the pair gets to move forward one square.

   • The first pair to reach FINISH wins.

3. Circulate during the activity to make sure students' answers are correct.

Extension

If some groups finish before the rest of the class, have each pair write directions to different places on the map. For example:

> Directions to the Hospital
>
> Go straight on Washington Street to Lakewood Drive. Turn right on Lakewood Drive. Go through two traffic lights. The hospital is on the left.

Answer Key

1. Are utilities included? Yes, (they are).
2. How much is the rent? $900 a month.
3. How many bedrooms are there? Two.
4. Is there a park nearby? Yes, there is.
5. Is a security deposit required? Yes. (1 month security)
6. Can you give me directions to the bookstore? *Answers will vary.*
7. Is there a bank nearby? No, there isn't.
8. Are pets allowed? No, they aren't.
9. Is there a laundry room in the basement? Yes, there is.
10. How many bathrooms are there? There's one bathroom.
11. Can you give me directions to the supermarket? *Answers will vary.*
12. Is there a bus stop nearby? Yes, there is.
13. Is there a parking garage? Yes, there is.
14. Can you give me directions to the post office? *Answers will vary.*
15. How much is the security deposit? $900.

Board Game: *Apartment for Rent*

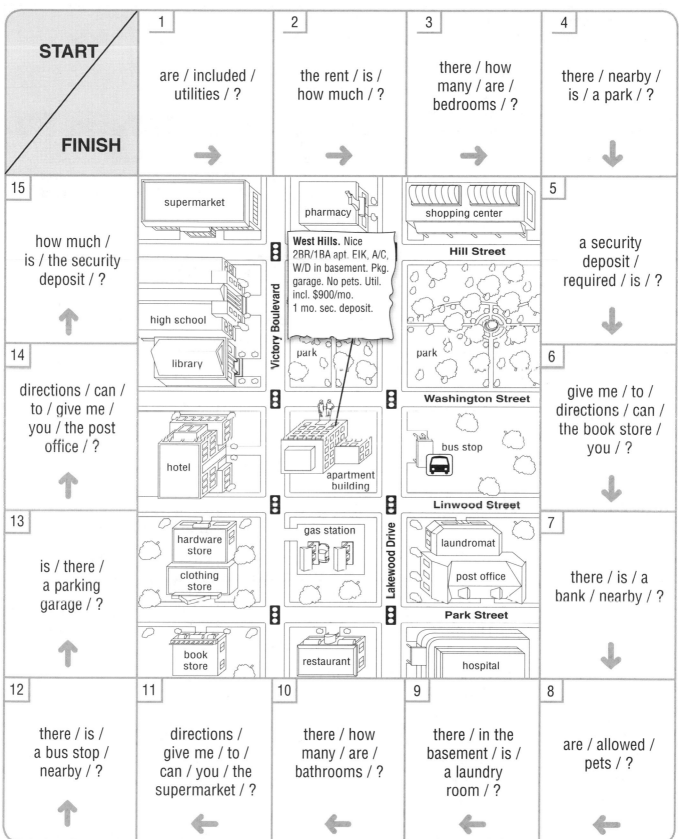

START

FINISH

1
are / included / utilities / ? →

2
the rent / is / how much / ? →

3
there / how many / are / bedrooms / ? →

4
there / nearby / is / a park / ? ↓

15
how much / is / the security deposit / ? ↑

5
a security deposit / required / is / ? ↓

supermarket

pharmacy

shopping center

Hill Street

West Hills. Nice 2BR/1BA apt. EIK, A/C, W/D in basement. Pkg. garage. No pets. Util. incl. $900/mo. 1 mo. sec. deposit.

high school

park

park

Victory Boulevard

14
directions / can / to / give me / you / the post office / ? ↑

library

Washington Street

apartment building

bus stop

6
give me / to / directions / can / the book store / you / ? ↓

hotel

13
is / there / a parking garage / ? ↑

hardware store

clothing store

gas station

Linwood Street

laundromat

post office

Lakewood Drive

7
there / is / a bank / nearby / ? ↓

book store

restaurant

Park Street

hospital

12
there / is / a bus stop / nearby / ? ↑

11
directions / give me / to / can / you / the supermarket / ? ←

10
there / how many / are / bathrooms / ? ←

9
there / in the basement / is / a laundry room / ? ←

8
are / allowed / pets / ? ←

Build a Sentence: *Last Weekend*

Grouping	Pairs
Target Language	Regular verbs in the simple past, past activities
Materials	Activity Master 26
Class Time	20 minutes

Teacher Preparation

- Copy Activity Master 26, one for each pair of students.

- Cut each copy into 20 cards. The white cards are sentence beginnings and the gray cards are sentence endings.

  Note: You may only want to start with only the first five pairs.

- Clip each set of cards together.

Procedure

1. Put students in like-ability pairs. Give a set of cards to each pair.

2. Tell Student A to shuffle the white cards and Student B to shuffle the gray cards. Have students put their cards face up on their desks.

3. Explain that students are going to work together to make ten (or five) correct sentences with the cards. Tell students that the white cards are sentence beginnings and the gray cards are sentence endings.

4. Model the activity. Assemble a white card and a gray card into a correct sentence and read it aloud: *Last weekend I invited some friends over for a barbecue.*

5. Write the sentence on the board. Tell students to assemble the sentence with their cards.

6. Tell students to continue to assemble correct sentences.

7. Circulate during the activity to make sure students' matched sentences are correct.

Multilevel Option

Pre-level: Give pre-level students only the first ten cards so that they have fewer choices to consider as they match the cards. When they finish the first half of the cards, give them the second half.

Extension

If some pairs complete the activity before the rest of the class, have them look at each sentence they wrote and say whether it is true for them. For example:

> A: *Last night I listened to music. Yes, that's true for me. It is true for you?*
>
> B: *Yes, it is. Last weekend I baked cookies. No, that's not true for me. I didn't bake cookies last weekend. Did you?*
>
> A: *No, I didn't.*

Variation

Mixer: Use one copy of Activity Master 26. Give each student a card at random. Have students walk around the classroom. They continually say their half of the sentence until they find the matching half. If there are more than 20 students, use two copies of Activity Master 26.

Build a Sentence: *Last Weekend*

1. Last weekend I invited	some friends over for a barbecue.
2. Last night I watched	a movie on TV.
3. Last night I cooked	dinner for my family.
4. Last weekend I cleaned	my apartment.
5. Last night I stayed	up late.
6. Last weekend I baked	cookies.
7. Last night I finished	my homework before dinner.
8. Last weekend I walked	my dog in the park.
9. Last night I listened	to music.
10. Last weekend I called	my mother.

Unit 6 • Lesson 6

Find Someone Who: *Milestones*

Grouping Whole-class mixer
Target Language Milestones, *yes / no* questions in simple past, irregular form of simple past verbs
Materials Activity Master 27
Class Time 20 minutes

Teacher Preparation

Copy Activity Master 27, one for each student.

Procedure

1. Give a copy of Activity Master 27 to each student.

2. Explain that students are going to walk around the classroom. They will ask and answer *Did you _____?* in order to complete as many sentences on Activity Master 00 as possible. Tell students they will have 15 minutes for the activity.

3. Write *Did you _____?* on the board. Have them complete the question for the first item, *Did you grow up in a big city?* You may want to point out that the verb changes in the question form. Walk around the classroom, asking students *Did you grow up in a big city?* until you get a *yes* answer. Write the student's name to complete the first sentence on the board.

4. Circulate during the activity to help students formulate questions correctly.

Multilevel Options

Pre-level: Have *all* students compose the questions for the activity before they begin to circulate around the classroom. This will make it easier for the pre-level students to participate in the activity.

Above-level: To increase the difficulty for above-level students, have them write three additional sentence prompts to extend the activity. For example:

_____ had a small store in Mexico.

Extension

After the class has finished the activity, have students read their sentences aloud so the class can learn about people they didn't have a chance to talk to.

Variation

Have students do the activity in groups of 4. After 5 minutes, have students report to the class what they learned about their group members. The rest of the class listens and completes Activity Master 27.

Find Someone Who: *Milestones*

Name	
	grew up in a big city.
	grew up in a small village.
	went to school in a small village.
	took English classes in his / her country.
	studied English in high school.
	got his / her first job at age 16.
	had a small business in his / her country.
	came to the United States before 2007.
	came to the United States one year ago.
	always wanted to live in the United States.
	found a good job quickly in the United States.
	moved into a new apartment last year.
	got married two years ago.
	had a big wedding
	got married in the United States.

Picture-based Story: *Lisa*

Grouping	Pairs and then whole class
Target Language	Simple past, describing a person's milestones
Materials	Activity Master 28
Class Time	25 minutes

Teacher Preparation

Copy Activity Master 28, one for each student.

Procedure

1. Give a copy of Activity Master 28 to each student.

2. Explain that students are going to write a story based on the pictures.

3. Put students in cross-ability pairs to discuss the questions on Activity Master 28.

4. Have students report their ideas to the class. Make sure students understand the scenes:

   (1) Lisa was born.

   (2) Lisa grew up.

   (3) She graduated from school.

   (4) She got a job.

   (5) She got married.

   (6) She and her husband had children.

5. Ask the class: *What's the story?* Have the class develop a <u>general</u> story line orally. Write key vocabulary words on the board.

6. Have students return to working in pairs to write a draft of their story <u>with their own original details</u>. Circulate around the classroom helping students with their writing.

7. As students finish their stories, put them together with another pair to share their stories and give one another feedback.

8. Have students write a final copy of their story to submit to you for your corrections and feedback.

Multilevel Options

Pre-level: Have students write only two sentences for each picture.

Above-level: Challenge students to add many details and to write four to five sentences for each picture.

Extension

After they finish their story, have students write comprehension questions about their story. Then have students exchange their stories and questions. Have them read their classmates' stories, answer the questions, and then check their answers with the student authors.

Picture-based Story: *Lisa*

- When was Lisa born?
- Where was Lisa born?
- What are the names of her parents?
- Was she their first daughter?

- Where did Lisa grow up?
- Did she have many brothers and sisters?
- Was she happy?

- How old was Lisa when she graduated?
- Did she do well in school?
- What kind of school did she graduate from?

- What was Lisa's first job?
- Was she happy in her job?
- How long did she work at her first job?

- When did Lisa meet her husband?
- What is his name?
- Where did they get married?
- Did they have a big wedding?

- What are the names of their children?
- How old is Lisa's son?
- Is her second child a boy or a girl?
- Does Lisa still have a job?

1. **PAIRS: Discuss the questions under each picture.**

2. **CLASS: Tell the story to the teacher. Write down the new vocabulary.**

3. **PAIRS: Write your story together.**

Information Gap: *A Family Love Story*

Grouping Pairs
Target Language *Wh-* questions in the simple past, regular and irregular verbs in the simple past
Materials Activity Master 29
Class Time 20 minutes

Teacher Preparation

- Copy Activity Master 29, one for every two students.

- Cut each copy into two parts. Clip together Card A and Card B.

Procedure

1. Put students in like-ability pairs. Give a copy of Card A to Student A and a copy of Card B to Student B in each pair.

2. Explain that students are going to ask and answer questions to complete the story.

3. Write *When* _____ ? on the board. Have them complete the question for the first item, *When did Bill move to Spain?* You may want to point out that the verb changes in the question form. Then model the activity. Play the part of Student A. Call on an above-level student to play the part of Student B:

   A: *When did Bill move to Spain?*

   B: *He moved to Spain in 2007.*

   A: *In 2007?*

   B: *Yes.*

   Instruct all Student As to write *2007* in the blank on line 1 of their cards.

4. Have pairs continue the activity. Tell students that they should not show each other their cards.

5. Circulate during the activity to help students form the correct questions and to make sure they do not show their partners their cards until the end of the activity.

6. When the pairs have shared all their information, have them compare their cards to check their information. The stories on Cards A and B should be the same.

Multilevel Options

Pre-level: Have pre-level students meet with students who have the same card. (Card A students sit together. Card B students sit together.) Have the students work together to write the questions for each blank on their card. Then have them meet with a person with a different card to ask and answer the questions.

Above-level: Have above-level students fold the question words under their card so they have to form the question independently.

Extension

If some pairs finish before the rest of the class, have them write a love story they have in their own family.

Information Gap: *A Family Love Story*

Card A: *A Family Love Story*

1. Bill moved to Spain in _____.   **when**

2. He moved there because he got a job in Spain.   **why**

3. He met a woman named Maria at _____.   **where**

4. They knew immediately that they were perfect for each other.   **what**

5. In _____ they got married.   **when**

6. They had a big wedding.   **what**

7. Bill's family came to Spain because _____.   **why**

8. Bill's brother met Maria's sister at the wedding.   **where**

9. In _____ Bill's and Maria's families went to another wedding in Spain.   **when**

10. This time Bill's brother and Maria's sister _____!   **what**

Card B: *A Family Love Story*

1. Bill moved to Spain in 2007.   **when**

2. He moved there because _____.   **why**

3. He met a woman named Maria at his new job.   **where**

4. They knew immediately that _____.   **what**

5. In 2008 they got married.   **when**

6. They had a _____.   **what**

7. Bill's family came to Spain because they wanted to meet Maria.   **why**

8. Bill's brother met Maria's sister at _____.   **where**

9. In 2009 Bill's and Maria's families went to another wedding in Spain.   **when**

10. This time Bill's brother and Maria's sister got married!   **what**

Board Game: *Talking About the Past*

Grouping Groups of 4
Target Language Asking and answering questions about past events and activities, simple past of regular and irregular verbs
Materials Activity Master 30, a coin, two markers for each group
Class Time 20 minutes

Teacher Preparation

Copy Activity Master 30, one for every four students.

Procedure

1. Put students in like-ability pairs. Each pair is a team. Put two teams together to play the game. Give each group of 4 a copy of Activity Master 30, a coin, and two markers.

2. Explain that students are going to play a board game. Here are the rules:

   • Pair 1 flips a coin to move. *Heads* means the team moves the marker ahead two squares and *tails* means the team moves their marker ahead one square.

   • Pair 1 moves the marker to a square. Student A forms the question. Student B answers with true information. Pair 2 listens to make sure Pair 1's question and answer are correct.

   • If Pair 1's question and answer are correct, Pair 2 takes a turn.

   • If Pair 1's question and answer are incorrect, Pair 1 moves the marker back one square, and Pair 2 takes a turn.

   • If a pair lands on a square that already has a marker on it, the pair gets to move forward one square.

   • The first pair to reach FINISH wins.

3. Circulate during the activity to make sure students' answers are grammatically correct.

Extension

If some groups finish before the rest of the class, have each student write three true sentences about their partner. For example:

> Felix didn't cook dinner last night.
>
> Felix took the bus to school.
>
> He got to school at 5:30.

Answer Key

1. What did you do last night?

2. Where did you study English last year?

3. Did you finish all your homework last night?

4. What time did you get to school today?

5. Why did you come to the United States?

6. When did you move here?

7. What did you cook for dinner last night?

8. Where did you grow up?

9. What time did you go to sleep last night/

10. What did you have for breakfast this morning?

11. Did you take a bus to school today?

12. Where did you go on your last vacation?

13. Did you grow up in a small village?

14. Did you oversleep this morning?

Board Game: *Talking About the Past*

	1	2	3
START	What / you / do / last night? →	Where / you / study / English / last year? →	you / finish / all your homework / last night? ↓
7 What / you / cook / for dinner last night? ↓	6 When / you / move / here? ←	5 Why / you / come / to the U.S.? ←	4 What time / you / get / to school today? ←
8 Where / you / grow up? →	9 What time / you / go to sleep / last night? →	10 What / you / have / for breakfast / this morning? →	11 you / take / a bus / to school today? ↓
FINISH	14 you / oversleep / this morning? ←	13 you / grow up / in a small village? ←	12 Where / you / go / on your last vacation? ←

Tic-Tac-Toe: *Talking about medical appointments with* on / at / by / in / from . . . to

Grouping	Groups of four
Target Language	Talking about medical appointments, using prepositions of time: *on / at / by / in / from . . . to*
Materials	Activity Master 31
Class Time	20 minutes

Teacher Preparation

Copy Activity Master 31, one for every four students.

Procedure

1. Put students in like-ability pairs. Each pair is a team. Put two teams together to play the game. Give each group of four a copy of Activity Master 31.

2. Explain that students are going to play Tic-Tac-Toe with correct sentences using the words in the Tic-Tac-Toe grids. Here are the rules:

   • A student on Team 1 points to a square in the grid (for example, office / be / closed / 1:00–2:00) and then makes a correct sentence with those words (for example, *The office is closed from 1:00 to 2:00.*) Team 2 decides if the sentence is correct. If the sentence is correct, Team 1 marks an X over that time phrase in the grid.

   • Team 2 takes a turn by pointing to another square on the grid and making a correct sentence. If the sentence is correct, Team 2 marks an O over that time phrase in the grid.

   • The first team to get three marks in a row—vertically, horizontally, or diagonally—wins.

3. Circulate during the activity to make sure that students' sentences are correct.

4. Have teams play a second round.

Extension

If some groups finish before the rest of the class, have pairs write all the sentences in the grid.

Answer Key

Round 1

The office is closed from 1:00 to 2:00.

My appointment is in the morning.

You need to get here at / by 10:15.

The doctor wants to see you in ten days.

The clinic is open from Monday to Friday.

Can you come on Wednesday afternoon?

Dr. Pataki has openings on July 21 and July 23.

You need to come back in three days.

We close at noon.

Round 2

You need to come back in five weeks.

The doctor is not available from January 25 to February 2.

The dentist can see you in a few minutes.

The doctor has an opening at 4:15.

My daughter has a check-up on Tuesday afternoon.

The pharmacy is open from 8:00 to 6:00.

You need to arrive at the office at / by 3:40.

The nurse can call you in the evening.

I have an appointment on November 6.

Tic-Tac-Toe: *Talking about medical appointments with* on / at / by / in / from . . . to

Round 1

office / be / closed / 1:00–2:00	my appointment / be / the morning	you / need / get here / 10:15
doctor / want / see you / ten days	clinic / open / Mon.–Fri.	can / you / come / Wednesday afternoon?
Dr. Pataki / have / openings / July 21 and July 23	you / need / come back / three days	we / close / noon

Round 2

you / need / come back / five weeks	doctor / not be available / Jan. 25–Feb. 2	dentist / can / see you / a few minutes
doctor / have / opening / 4:15	my daughter / have / check-up / Tuesday afternoon	pharmacy / be / open / 8:00–6:00
you / need / arrive / at the office / 3:40	nurse / can / call / you / the evening	I / have / blood test / Nov. 6

Unit 7 • Lesson 6

Miming Game: *What's the matter?*

Grouping	Groups of three students
Target Language	Identifying health problems, simple present tense, simple past
Materials	Activity Master 32
Class Time	15 minutes

Teacher Preparation

• Copy Activity Master 32, one for every three students.

• Cut each copy into 15 cards and clip each set together.

Procedure

1. Put students in like-ability groups. Give a set of cards to each group.

2. Explain that students are going to take turns picking up a card and miming the health problem on the card. The team guesses the problem and writes it in a correct sentence on the board.

3. Model the activity. Invite two students to come to the board with you. You take the role of Student A. For example:

   A: [Picks up a card and begins to mime a headache.]

   B: *You have a headache*

   A: *Yes. Write it down.*

   C: [Writes *You have a headache.* on the board.]

   A: [Compares the sentence on the board to the one on the card to make sure the sentence on the board is correct.]

   Note: Teams must erase the sentence once they have checked it.

4. Continue to model the activity. This time pick one of the three cards that describes an injury.

   A: [Picks up a card and begins to mime biting into a sandwich and then breaking a tooth.]

   B: *You broke your tooth.*

   A: *Yes.*

   C: [Writes *You broke your tooth.* on the board.]

   A: [Compares the sentence on the board to the one on the card to make sure the sentence on the board is correct.]

5. Circulate during the activity to help teams identify errors in their sentences and to remind teams to erase their sentences after each turn.

Multilevel Option

Pre-level: Have pre-level students write only the health problem and not the complete sentence. For example:

   headache

   dizzy

Extension

If some teams finish before the rest of the class, have them work together to write a list of all the health problems they can remember without looking at the cards. Have them submit their lists to you for your spelling corrections.

Variation

Have students do the activity in groups of 4.

Miming Game: *What's the matter?*

You have a headache.	Your arms are itchy.
You have a sore throat.	You're dizzy.
You have a cough.	Your eye is swollen.
You have a fever.	You're nauseous.
You have heartburn.	You sprained your ankle.
You have a stiff neck.	You broke your tooth.
You have an earache.	You cut your finger.
You have chest pains.	

Picture-based Story: *Bad Habits*

Grouping	Pairs and then whole class
Target Language	Talking about habits that contribute to stress and ways to reduce stress
Materials	Activity Master 33
Class Time	25 minutes

Teacher Preparation

Copy Activity Master 33, one for each student.

Procedure

1. Give a copy of Activity Master 33 to each student.

2. Explain that students are going to write a conversation based on the information in the pictures.

3. Put students in cross-ability pairs to discuss the questions about the pictures on Activity Master 33.

4. Have students report their ideas to the class. Make sure students understand the scenes:

   (1) Dan is a bus driver. He works at night. He works a lot.

   (2) Dan lives alone. He's eating junk food for dinner while watching TV.

   (3) Dan can't sleep. He's worried about money. He's thinking about his bills.

   (4) Dan goes to see his doctor. He's worried about his health.

5. Ask the class: *What is causing stress in Dan's life? What does the doctor tell Dan?* Write key vocabulary words on the board.

6. Have students return to working in pairs to write a draft of their conversation between Dan and his doctor. Circulate around the classroom helping students with their writing.

7. As students finish their written conversations, put them together with another pair to share their writing and give one another feedback.

8. Have students write a final copy of their written conversation to submit to you for your corrections and feedback.

Multilevel Option

Above-level: Have above-level students be the scribes in their pairs.

Extension

Have students role-play the conversation between Dan and his doctor.

Picture-based Story: *Bad Habits*

- What is Dan's job?
- Is it stressful work? Why?

- What is Dan doing?
- Is this a healthy habit? Why not?

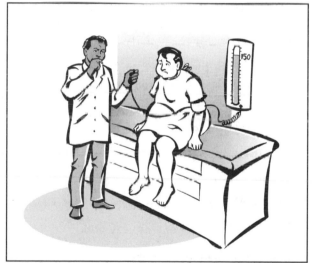

- Why isn't Dan sleeping?
- What is he thinking about?

- Where is Dan?
- How is his health?
- What is the doctor going to say to Dan?

1. **PAIRS: Discuss the questions under each picture.**

2. **CLASS: Talk aboout the pictures with the teacher. Write down the new vocabulary.**

3. **PAIRS: Write the conservation between Dan and his doctor together.**

Unit 7 • Lesson 9

Survey: *Reasons for Missing Class or Being Late*

Grouping Whole-class mixer
Target Language Ways to express reasons, simple past
Materials Activity Master 34
Class Time 20 minutes

Teacher Preparation

Copy Activity Master 34, one for each student.

Procedure

1. Give a copy of Activity Master 34 to each student.

2. Explain that students are going to walk around the classroom to take a survey. Students will ask each other about why they missed classes or were late for class. They will write the information in the chart on Activity Master 34. Tell students they will have 15 minutes for the activity.

3. Brainstorm with the class some possible reasons students miss class or are late for class and write them on the board. For example:

   Because I had to work.

   Because I had to take care of my daughter.

   Because I was sick.

   Because I had to take my sister to the clinic.

   Because the weather was very bad.

   Because I had car trouble.

   Because I missed the bus.

4. Play the part of Student A. Call on an above-level student to play the part of Student B. Then model the activity:

   A: *Toni, did you ever miss a class?*

   B: *Yes.*

   A: *Why did you miss the class?*

   B: *Because I had to take my son to the clinic.*

   A: [Writes name and reason in chart.]

   Write Student B's answer on the board.

5. Continue to play the role of Student A. Walk around the classroom. Stop at the desk of another above-level student. Ask him or her to play the part of Student C. Ask Student C when and why he or she missed a class. Write Student C's answers on the board.

6. Circulate during the activity to help students with new vocabulary and spelling of words.

Multilevel Options

Pre-level: During the activity, have pre-level students refer to the vocabulary on the board as they write their classmates' answers.

Above-level: Tell above-level students to do the activity without looking at the vocabulary on the board.

Extension

After the class has finished the activity, have students look at the information in their survey and discuss the following questions:

What are the most common reasons for missing class?

What are the most common reasons for being late to class?

What can students do to come to class more often?

Survey: *Reasons for Missing Class or Being Late*

Did you ever miss a class?
Why did you miss the class?

Name	Reason for missing class

Were you ever late to class?
Why were you late?

Name	Reason for being late

Board Game: *Conversations About Your Health*

Grouping	Groups of 4
Target Language	Identifying health problems, making a doctor's appointment, talking about medicine labels, talking about an injury
Materials	Activity Master 35, a coin, two markers for each group
Class Time	25 minutes

Teacher Preparation

Copy Activity Master 35, one for every four students.

Procedure

1. Put students in like-ability pairs. Each pair is a team. Put two teams together to play the game. Give each group of 4 a copy of Activity Master 10, a coin, and two markers.

2. Explain that students are going to play a board game. They have to form a conversation using the line in the box that they land in. Here are the rules:

   • Pair 1 flips a coin to move. *Heads* means the team moves the marker ahead two squares and *tails* means the team moves their marker ahead one square.

   • Pair 1 moves the marker to a square. They read the line and have to use that line in a correct conversation. For example:

      (Thanks for calling.)

      A: *I can't come in today because I have to go to the doctor. I don't feel well.*

      B: *That's too bad. Thanks for calling.*

Pair 2 listens to make sure Pair 1's conversation is correct. If Pair 1's conversation is correct, Pair 2 takes a turn.

   • If Pair 1's conversation is incorrect, Pair 1 moves the marker back one square, and Pair 2 takes a turn.

   • If a pair lands on a square that already has a marker on it, the pair gets to move forward one square.

   • The first pair to reach FINISH wins.

3. Circulate during the activity to make sure students' conversations are correct.

Multilevel Option

Pre-level: Allow the pairs of students 10 minutes to read all the lines on the game board and look in the unit in the Student Book to take some notes to help them during the game. This will help the pre-level student prepare for the challenge of this game.

Board Game: *Conversations About Your Health*

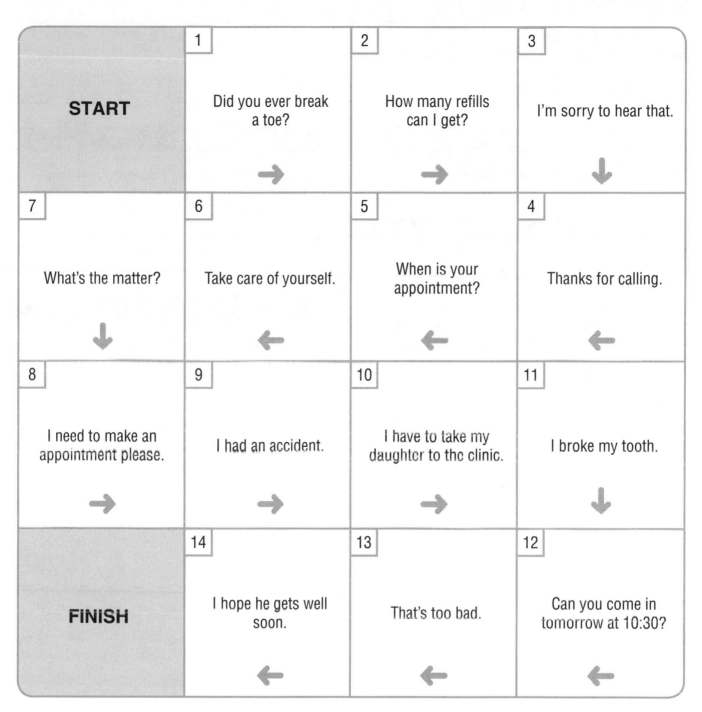

	1 Did you ever break a toe? →	2 How many refills can I get? →	3 I'm sorry to hear that. ↓
START			
7 What's the matter? ↓	6 Take care of yourself. ←	5 When is your appointment? ←	4 Thanks for calling. ←
8 I need to make an appointment please. →	9 I had an accident. →	10 I have to take my daughter to the clinic. →	11 I broke my tooth. ↓
FINISH	14 I hope he gets well soon. ←	13 That's too bad. ←	12 Can you come in tomorrow at 10:30? ←

Interview: *Skill Inventory*

Grouping	Pairs
Target Language	Identifying job skills, *can* for ability
Materials	Activity Master 36
Class Time	20 minutes

Teacher Preparation

Copy Activity Master 36, one for each student.

Procedure

1. Put students in like-ability pairs and give a copy of Activity Master 36 to each student.

2. Explain that students are going to complete the inventory about their own skills and then talk to their partners about their skills. Tell students they will have 5 minutes to complete their inventory and 10 minutes to talk with and listen to their partner.

3. Play the part of Student A. Call on an above-level student to play the part of Student B. Then model the activity:

   A: *Can you use a computer?*

   B: *Yes, I can. Can you?*

   A: *Yes, I can.*

   A & B: [Mark a check in both columns for number 1.]

   B: *Can you install computer software?*

   A: *No, I can't.*

4. Circulate during the activity to make sure students listen to one another and complete the information about their partner's skills.

Multilevel Options

Pre-level: Have the pairs work together to read each line and check the columns together.

Above-level: To increase the difficulty for above-level pairs, have them ask the questions out of order so that they have to listen to one another carefully.

Extension

- If some students finish before others, have them look at the skills on Activity Master 36 and decide which ones a person uses in the following workplaces: an office, a store, a restaurant, and a warehouse.

- After the class has finished the activity, have students circle the skills they don't have but want to learn. Ask students to tell the class three skills they want to learn.

Interview: *Skill Inventory*

Skill	Me	My Partner
I can . . .	Yes ✓ No X	Yes ✓ No X
1. use a computer.		
2. install computer hardware.		
3. use a word-processing program.		
4. type.		
5. speak two languages.		
6. answer the phone in English.		
7. record information.		
8. prepare food.		
9. lift heavy boxes.		
10. operate a forklift.		
11. plan work schedules.		
12. greet customers.		
13. operate a cash register.		
14. assist customers.		
15. stock shelves.		
16. order supplies.		

Information Gap: *Tom's Work History*

Grouping	Pairs
Target Language	Time expressions with *in* and *later*, simple past, asking and answering questions about work history
Materials	Activity Master 37
Class Time	20 minutes

Teacher Preparation

• Copy Activity Master 37, one for every two students.

• Cut each copy into two parts. Clip together Time Line A and Time Line B.

Procedure

1. Put students in like-ability pairs. Give a copy of Time Line A to Student A and a copy of Time Line B to Student B in each pair.

2. Hold up a copy of Time Line A. Explain that students are going to fill in the missing information in their time lines by asking each other about Tom's work history.

3. Play the part of Student A. Call on an above-level student to play the part of Student B. Then model the activity:

   A: *What happened in June 1994?*

   B: *Tom graduated from high school.*

   A: *He graduated from high school?* [Writes down information.]

   B: *Yes.*

   Instruct all Student As to write *graduated from high school* on the first line of their time lines.

4. Continue to model the activity:

   B: *When did Tom come to the United States?*

   A: *He came in July 1996.*

   B: [Writes down information.]

   Instruct all Student Bs to write July *1996* on the second line of their time lines.

5. Have pairs continue the activity. Tell students not to show each other their time lines.

6. Circulate during the activity to help students with spelling and to make sure they do not show their partners their time lines until the end of the activity.

7. After pairs have filled in their time lines, have partners compare cards to check their information. The information on both cards should be the same.

Multilevel Options

Pre-level: Encourage pre-level students to refer to the question box on their time line cards for guidance during the activity.

Above-level: Have above-level students fold the question box under the time line and form the questions on their own.

Extension

If some pairs finish before the rest of the class, have them write sentences about Tom's work history. For example:

In 1994 Tom graduated from high school. He came to the United States two years later, in 1996.

Information Gap: *Tom's Work History*

Time Line A		Time Line B	
June 1994		June 1994	graduated from high school
July 1996	came to the United States		came to the United States
	started English classes	2 months later	started English classes
October 1996	got a job in a warehouse	October 1996	
1997		1997	learned to operate a forklift
1998	became a supervisor		became a supervisor
	started computer classes	2000	started computer classes
April 2002	lost his job because warehouse moved	April 2002	
1 month later		1 month later	got a part-time job in a restaurant
January 15, 2003	graduated from computer school		graduated from computer school
3 weeks later	got a job as a computer system analyst	3 weeks later	
2009		2009	started his own company

Example Questions

When did Tom *start English classes*?

What happened in *1997*?

What happened *1 month later*?

Example Questions

When did Tom *come to the United States*?

What happened in *October 1996*?

What happened *3 weeks later*?

Picture-based Story: *The New Job Market*

Grouping Pairs and then whole class
Target Language Simple past
Materials Activity Master 38
Class Time 25 minutes

Teacher Preparation

Copy Activity Master 38, one for each student.

Procedure

1. Give a copy of Activity Master 38 to each student.

2. Explain that students are going to write a story based on the pictures.

3. Put students in cross-ability pairs to discuss the questions on Activity Master 38.

4. Have students report their ideas to the class. Make sure students understand the scenes:

   (1) Lao got his first job in a factory. He started his job in 1982.

   (2) Lao became a supervisor in the factory. It was a good job.

   (3) Lao worked at the factory for 28 years. Then the factory closed, and Lao lost his job.

   (4) Lao is looking for a job. He doesn't have the right job skills for a good job.

5. Ask the class: *What's the story?* Have the class develop a <u>general</u> story line orally. Write key vocabulary words on the board.

6. Have students return to working in pairs to write a draft of their story. Circulate around the classroom, helping students with their writing.

7. As students finish their stories, put them together with another pair to share their stories and give one another feedback.

8. Have students write a final copy of their story to submit to you for your corrections and feedback.

Multilevel Option

Above-level: Have above-level students be the scribes in their pairs.

Extension

- Have students cut out the pictures, making a three-page story with a picture and text on each page. Have them share their books with the class.

- After they finish their story, have students write comprehension questions about their story. Then have students exchange their stories and questions. Have them read their classmates' stories, answer the questions, and then check their answers with the student authors.

Picture-based Story: *The New Job Market*

- When did Lao start his first job?
- What kind of work did he do?

- What was Lao's second job?
- When did he get that job?
- Was it a good job?

- What happened to Lao's job?
- When did the factory close?
- How many years did Lao work at the factory?

- What job skills does Lao have?
- What kind of job can Lao do?
- What jobs are available?
- What happens next?

1. **PAIRS: Discuss the questions under each picture.**

2. **CLASS: Tell the story to the teacher. Write down the new vocabulary.**

3. **PAIRS: Write your story together.**

Unit 8 • Lesson 9

Put in Order: *A Job Interview*

Grouping Pairs
Target Language Identifying job duties, talking about job skills, answering questions about work history and job availability
Materials Activity Master 39
Class Time 20 minutes

Teacher Preparation

- Copy Activity Master 39, one for each pair of students.

- Cut each copy into 14 cards. The white cards are Speaker A and the gray cards are Speaker B.

  Note: For pre-level students, cut only Speaker B's lines into cards. Leave Speaker A's card intact, so that pre-level students can focus on finding the appropriate responses.

- Clip each set of cards together.

Procedure

1. Put students in like-ability pairs. Give a set of cards to each pair.

2. Tell Student A to shuffle the white cards and Student B to shuffle the gray cards. Have students put their cards face up on their desks.

3. Explain that students are going to work together to put a job interview conversation in order. Tell students that Speaker A begins the conversation (white cards).

4. Model the activity. Pull out a Speaker A card with a question, for example: *I have your application here. I see that you are working now. What are your job duties?* Ask the class to look for the response in the B cards (gray cards). When a student finds it, have the student call it out so everyone can find it. *I greet and assist customers. Also, I stock the shelves.*

5. Tell students to continue in pairs to find Speaker A's next prompt.

6. Circulate during the activity to make sure students are putting the job interview conversation in the correct order.

Multilevel Option

Pre-level: Do not cut Speaker A's lines into cards, but rather leave them as a block in their correct order. This way pre-level students can focus on finding Speak B's responses and not worry about putting the conversation in order.

Extension

If some pairs complete the activity before the rest of the class, have partners take turns picking up a white card and asking their partner the question or prompt. The partner responds talking about his or her own work skills and experience.

Put in Order: *A Job Interview*

A: I have your application here. I see that you are working now. What are your job duties?

B: I greet and assist customers. Also, I stock the shelves.

A: OK. Tell me about your skills. Can you use a computer?

B: No, I can't, but I can learn.

A: Tell me more about your work experience.

B: I came to the United States six years ago. First, I got a job as a food service worker. Then last year I got a job as a sales associate.

A: So now you're a sales associate. Why are you looking for another job?

B: Things in my life have changed, and now I'd like to make more money.

A: Let me ask a few questions about your availability. Do you prefer days or evenings?

B: Well, I prefer days, but I'm flexible.

A: Can you work on the weekends?

B: No, I can't.

A: When could you start?

B: In ten days. I need to give ten days' notice at my job.

Board Game: *The Working World*

Grouping Groups of 4

Target Language Identifying job duties, answering questions about work history, talking about job skills, answering questions about availability

Materials Activity Master 40, a coin, two markers for each group

Class Time 20 minutes

Teacher Preparation

Copy Activity Master 40, one for every four students.

Procedure

1. Put students in like-ability pairs. Each pair is a team. Put two teams together to play the game. Give each group of 4 a copy of Activity Master 40, a coin, and two markers.

2. Explain that students are going to play a board game. Here are the rules:

   • Pair 1 flips a coin to move. *Heads* means the team moves the marker ahead two squares and *tails* means the team moves their marker ahead one square.

   • Pair 1 moves the marker to a square. Student A reads the question aloud. Student B answers with true information. Pair 2 listens to make sure Pair 1's answer is appropriate and correct.

   • If Pair 1's answer is correct, Pair 2 takes a turn.

   • If Pair 1's answer is incorrect, Pair 1 moves the marker back one square, and Pair 2 takes a turn.

   • If a pair lands on a square that already has a marker on it, the pair gets to move forward one square.

   • The first pair to reach FINISH wins.

3. Circulate during the activity to make sure students' answers are correct.

Multilevel Option

Pre-level: Allow the pairs of students 10 minutes to read all the lines on the game board and look in the text to take some notes to help them during the game. This will help the pre-level student prepare for the challenge of this game.

Board Game: *The Working World*

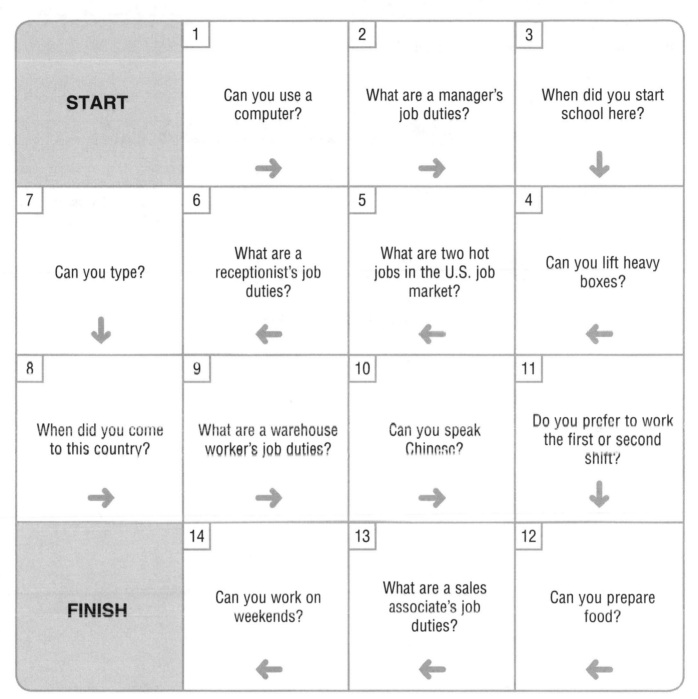

START	**1** Can you use a computer? →	**2** What are a manager's job duties? →	**3** When did you start school here? ↓
7 Can you type? ↓	**6** What are a receptionist's job duties? ←	**5** What are two hot jobs in the U.S. job market? ←	**4** Can you lift heavy boxes? ←
8 When did you come to this country? →	**9** What are a warehouse worker's job duties? →	**10** Can you speak Chinese? →	**11** Do you prefer to work the first or second shift? ↓
FINISH	**14** Can you work on weekends? ←	**13** What are a sales associate's job duties? ←	**12** Can you prepare food? ←

Unit 9 • Lesson 3

Information Gap: *Can you meet on Monday?*

Grouping	Pairs
Target Language	Future with *will*, making plans
Materials	Activity Master 41
Class Time	20 minutes

Teacher Preparation

- Copy Activity Master 41, one for every two students.

- Cut each copy into two parts. Clip together Schedule A and Schedule B.

Procedure

1. Put students in like-ability pairs. Give a copy of Schedule A to Student A and a copy of Schedule B to Student B in each pair.

2. Explain that students need to find a time they can meet for a parent-teacher conference. Student A has the schedule of Paul's parent. Student B has the schedule of Paul's teacher. They need to meet for a half hour at the school to talk about Paul.

3. Write on the board:

   Can you meet on _____ at _____?

   Yes, I can.

   No I can't. I'll be at _____.

4. Play the part of Paul's parent (A). Call on an above-level student to play the part of Paul's teacher (B). Then model the activity:

   A: *Can you meet on Monday at 5:00?*

   B: *No I can't. I have an exercise class. Can you meet at 5:30 on Tuesday?*

5. Have pairs continue the activity.

6. Circulate during the activity to make sure students do not show their partners their schedules until the end of the activity.

7. When pairs have found a time they can meet, have partners compare schedules to make sure they're both free at the time they arranged.

Multilevel Option

Pre-level: Have *all* students circle the openings they have in their schedules so they can be ready to ask questions about their partner's availability. This will make it easier for the pre-level students to form the questions.

Answer Key

Possible meeting times:
Thursday at 5:30 P.M.
Friday at 5:00 P.M.
Tuesday at 5:00 P.M.
Early morning at 7:00 A.M.

Information Gap: *Can you meet on Monday?*

A: Schedule of Paul's Parent

Mon	Tues	Wed	Thurs	Fri
volunteer at bake sale 9:00–11:00	work 8:00–5:00		work 8:00–1:00	
work 12:00–5:00		work 12:00–5:00	PTO meeting 2:00–4:00	work 12:00–5:00
Paul's band practice 7:30–9:00	Paul's basketball game 5:30–8:00	computer class 6:00–9:00		PTO meeting 7:00–9:00

B: Schedule of Paul's Teacher

Mon	Tues	Wed	Thurs	Fri
work 7:30–4:30	work 7:30–4:30	work 7:30–12:00	work 7:30–4:30	work 7:30–2:30
		meeting 1:00–2:30		meeting 3:00–4:00
			meeting 4:30–5:30	
exercise class 5:00–6:30		exercise class 5:00–6:30		dinner with Michael 6:00

Unit 9 • Lesson 6

Tic-Tac-Toe: *Describing Classmates with Adjectives and Adverbs*

Grouping	Groups of four
Target Language	Adjectives and adverbs of manner
Materials	Activity Master 42
Class Time	20 minutes

Teacher Preparation

Copy Activity Master 42, one for every four students.

Procedure

1. Make sure all students know each other's names. You may want them to wear name tags during this activity.

2. Put students in like-ability pairs. Each pair is a team. Put two teams together to play the game. Give each group of four a copy of Activity Master 42.

3. Explain that students are going to play Tic-Tac-Toe with true sentences about their classmates using the adjectives and adverbs of manner in the Tic-Tac-Toe grids. Here are the rules:

   • A student on Team 1 points to an adjective or adverb of manner in the grid (for example, *carefully*) and then makes a true sentence about a classmate using that word (for example, *Gladys does her homework carefully.*) Team 2 decides if the sentence is both correct and true. If so, Team 1 marks an X over that word in the grid.

   • Team 2 takes a turn by pointing to an adjective or adverb and making a sentence about a classmate using that word. If the sentence is correct and true, Team 2 marks an O over the word in the grid.

   • The first team to get three marks in a row— vertically, horizontally, or diagonally—wins.

4. Circulate during the activity to make sure that students' sentences about their classmates are grammatically correct and true.

5. Have teams play a second round.

Extension

If some groups finish before the rest of the class, have students write sentences about themselves using the words in the grids. The sentences may be negative or positive. For example:

I don't speak English clearly.

I am quiet.

Tic-Tac-Toe: *Describing Classmates with Adjectives and Adverbs*

Round 1

carefully	creative	quick
good	quietly	hard
neatly	fast	clear

Round 2

quiet	quickly	well
creatively	hard	careful
neat	fast	clearly

Unit 9 • Lesson 7

Picture-based Story: *The Cost of a College Education*

Grouping Pairs and then whole class
Target Language College education, talking about financial aid
Materials Activity Master 43
Class Time 25 minutes

Teacher Preparation

Copy Activity Master 43, one for each student.

Procedure

1. Give a copy of Activity Master 43 to each student.

2. Explain that students are going to write a story based on the pictures.

3. Put students in cross-ability pairs to discuss the questions about the pictures on Activity Master 43.

4. Have students report their ideas to the class. Make sure students understand the scenes:

   (1) Carla works as a waitress in a restaurant.

   (2) Carla helps her family at home.

   (3) Carla is tired in class.

   (4) Carla is doing poorly in college.

   (5) Carla goes to talk to a financial-aid counselor.

5. Ask the class: *What's the story?* Write key vocabulary words on the board.

6. Have students return to working in pairs to write a draft of their story. Circulate around the classroom, helping students with their writing.

7. As students finish their stories, put them together with another pair to share their writing and give one another feedback.

8. Have students write a final copy of their story to submit to you for your corrections and feedback.

Multilevel Option

Above-level: Have above-level students be the scribes in their pairs.

Extension

Have students role-play the conversation between Carla and the financial-aid counselor.

Picture-based Story: *The Cost of a College Education*

- What is Carla's job?

- Is it an easy job?

- Who does Carla live with?

- How does she help her family?

- What is Carla studying?

- How is she doing in class?

- How is Carla doing in math class?

- Why is she having trouble in her classes?

- Why is Carla talking to a financial-aid counselor?

- What are they talking about?

1. PAIRS: Discuss the questions under each picture.

2. CLASS: Tell the story to the teacher. Write down the new vocabulary.

3. PAIRS: Write the story together.

Build a Sentence: *How is my child doing in school?*

Grouping	Pairs
Target Language	Discussing a child's behavior at school
Materials	Activity Master 44
Class Time	20 minutes

Teacher Preparation

- Copy Activity Master 44, one for each pair of students.

- Cut each copy into 20 cards. The white cards are sentence beginnings and the gray cards are sentence endings.

  Note: You may want to start with only the first five pairs.

- Clip each set of cards together.

Procedure

1. Put students in like-ability pairs. Give a set of cards to each pair.

2. Tell Student A to shuffle the white cards and Student B to shuffle the gray cards. Have students put their cards face up on their desks.

3. Explain that students are going to work together to make ten (or five) correct sentences with the cards. Tell students that the white cards are sentence beginnings and the gray cards are sentence endings.

4. Model the activity. Assemble a white card and a gray card into a correct sentence and read it aloud: *He gets along well with other children.*

5. Write the sentence on the board. Tell students to assemble the sentence with their cards.

6. Tell students to continue to assemble correct sentences.

7. Circulate during the activity to make sure students' matched sentences are correct.

Note: Refer to the activity master to see the correct sentence matches.

Multilevel Option

Pre-level: Give pre-level students only the first five pairs so that they have fewer choices to consider as they match the cards. When they finish the first half of the cards, give them the second half.

Extension

If some pairs complete the activity before the rest of the class, have them sort the sentences into two categories: *Good Behavior* and *Bad Behavior*.

Variation

Play *Concentration.* Have pairs place all the cards face down. Have them take turns picking up a sentence beginning and a sentence ending. Do they match? If not, have one student replace the cards face down and let the other student take a turn. If the student finds a match, that student keeps the sentence.

Note: Make sure students put the cards in the same place on the table since concentrating on their location is an important part of this game.

Build a Sentence: *How is my child doing in school?*

1. He gets	along well with other children.
2. He skips	classes.
3. He has	trouble in language arts.
4. He gets to	school late.
5. He fools	around in class.
6. She does	her homework very carefully.
7. She pays	attention in class.
8. She's	disrespectful to the teachers.
9. She bullies	other kids.
10. She studies	hard for tests.

Board Game: *Schools*

Grouping	Groups of 4
Target Language	Identify job duties, answer questions about work history, talk about job skills, answer questions about availability
Materials	Activity Master 45, a coin, two markers for each group
Class Time	20 minutes

Teacher Preparation

Copy Activity Master 45, one for every four students.

Procedure

1. Put students in like-ability pairs. Each pair is a team. Put two teams together to play the game. Give each group of 4 a copy of Activity Master 45, a coin, and two markers.

2. Explain that students are going to play a board game. Here are the rules:

   • Pair 1 flips a coin to move. *Heads* means the team moves the marker ahead two squares and *tails* means the team moves their marker ahead one square.

   • Pair 1 moves the marker to a square. Student A reads the question aloud. Student B answers it. Pair 2 listens to make sure Pair 1's answer is correct.

   • If Pair 1's answer is correct, Pair 2 takes a turn.

   • If Pair 1's answer is incorrect, Pair 1 moves the marker back one square, and Pair 2 takes a turn.

   • If a pair lands on a square that already has a marker on it, the pair gets to move forward one square.

   • The first pair to reach FINISH wins.

3. Circulate during the activity to make sure students' answers are correct.

Multilevel Option

Pre-level: Allow the pairs of students 5 minutes to read all the questions on the game board and look in the unit in the Student Book to find (and remember) the answers. This will help the pre-level student prepare for the challenge of this game.

Answer Key

1. *Any four of the following:* math, language arts/English, physical education, social studies/history, art, music, technology, world languages, and science.

2. *Any three of the following:* school play, science fair, international party, school bake sale

3. fast, well, quietly

5. $22,000

6. *Any four of the following:* bully other kids, not pay attention, not get along with others, fool around in class, be disrespectful, skip class, get to school late

7. Carefully, hard, poorly

8. *Any three of the following:* preschool, elementary school, middle school, and high school

10. *Any two of the following:* teacher, principal, guidance counselor

11. They can talk to their child's teachers, they can help with their child's homework, they can find a program to help with their child's homework

12. College, university, community college

14. Parent-Teacher Organization

Board Game: *Schools*

	1 What are four school subjects? →	**2** What are three kinds of school events? →	**3** What is the adverb form of these words? fast good quiet ↓
START			

7 What is the adverb form of these words? careful hard poor ↓	**6** What are four school behavior problems? ←	**5** How much does tuition usually cost at a private college? ←	**4** What are three things you do well in school? ←

8 What are three kinds of schools for children? →	**9** What is something you do poorly in school? →	**10** Who works in an elementary school? Name two people. →	**11** How can parents help their child in school? ↓

14 What is a PTO? ←	**13** What subject did you do well in when you were you were a child? ←	**12** What are three types of colleges? ←
FINISH		

Unit 10 • Lesson 3

Picture Match: *Are there any apples in your picture?*

Grouping	Whole-class mixer
Target Language	Ask for quantities of food, count and non-count nouns
Materials	Activity Master 46
Class Time	20 minutes

Teacher Preparation

- Copy Activity Master 00. Make two copies of the activity master if you have up to 12 students, or four copies if you have up to 24 students. You need to make sure you have two copies of each individual card for the activity to work.

- Cut each copy into six cards.

Procedure

1. Give one card to each student at random. Have students look at the picture of the food on the card.

2. Explain that students are going to walk around the classroom and ask about the food on their classmates' cards in order to find a matching card. Tell students not to show their cards to anyone. They will have 15 minutes for the activity.

3. Write the following model on the board:

   Are there any <u>apples</u> in your picture?

   > Yes, there are.

   > No, there aren't.

   How many <u>apples</u> are there?

   > There are <u>two</u>.

   Is there any <u>cereal</u> in your picture?

   > Yes, there is.

   How many <u>boxes</u> of <u>cereal</u> are there?

   > There are <u>two boxes</u> of <u>cereal</u>.

   > There is one <u>box</u> of <u>cereal</u>.

4. Play the part of Student A. Look at your card. Walk around the classroom. Ask an above-level student to play the part of Student B. Ask the questions on the board. Continue to call on above-level students until you get a match.

   Note: Remind students that they should continue to question students until they find a match.

5. Circulate during the activity to make sure students are not showing anyone their cards and are forming correct questions and responses.

6. When students find a match, give each student another card to continue the activity.

Multilevel Options

Pre-level: During the activity, allow pre-level students to refer to the model on the board.

Above-level: Tell above-level students to do the activity without looking at the model on the board.

Extension

After the class has finished the activity, have students write several sentences about what is in their picture. For example:

> In my picture, there are two boxes of cereal and three cans of tuna. There is also a bottle of oil.

Picture Match: *Are there any apples in your picture?*

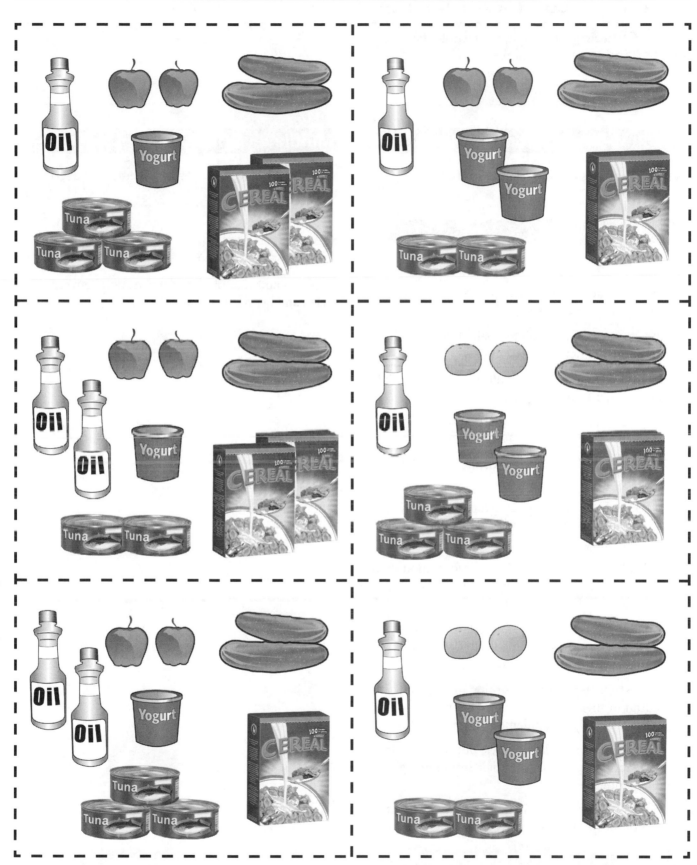

Picture-Based Story: *Thin Is In*

Grouping Pairs and then whole class
Target Language Nutrition
Materials Activity Master 47
Class Time 25 minutes

Teacher Preparation

Copy Activity Master 47, one for each student.

Procedure

1. Give a copy of Activity Master 47 to each student.

2. Explain that students are going to write a story based on the pictures.

3. Put students in cross-ability pairs to discuss the questions on Activity Master 47.

4. Have students report their ideas to the class. Make sure students understand the scenes:

   (1) Helen is looking at herself in the mirror. She thinks she is too heavy.

   (2) Helen stops eating food. She only drinks diet cola.

   (3) Helen is eating potato chips and drinking an energy drink. Her mother is worried about her.

   (4) Helen's mother gets some information about good nutrition. She and Helen make a plan to help Helen lose weight.

5. Ask the class: *What's the story?* Have the class develop a <u>general</u> story line orally. Write key vocabulary words on the board.

6. Have students return to working in pairs to write a draft of their story. Circulate around the classroom, helping students with their writing.

7. As students finish their stories, put them together with another pair to share their stories and give one another feedback.

8. Have students write a final copy of their story to submit to you for your corrections and feedback.

Multilevel Option

Above-level: Have above-level students be the scribes in their pairs.

Extension

Have students role-play the conversation between Helen and her mother.

Picture-based Story: *Thin Is In*

• What is Helen thinking?

• What is Helen eating?

• What is she drinking?

• What is Helen eating and drinking?

• What is her mother thinking?

• What is Helen's mother saying?

• How is Helen feeling now?

1. **PAIRS: Discuss the questions under each picture.**

2. **CLASS: Tell the story to the teacher. Write down the new vocabulary.**

3. **PAIRS: Write your story together.**

Question and Answer Game: *Compare Food Ads*

Grouping Pairs
Target Language Compare information in food ads, make a shopping list
Materials Activity Master 48
Class Time 20 minutes

Teacher Preparation

Copy Activity Master 48, one for each student.

Procedure

1. Put students in like-ability pairs. Give one copy of Activity Master 48 to each student.

2. Explain that students are going to compare supermarket prices and then make a shopping list for one of the stores. They can spend a total of $40. They will have 15 minutes to do the activity.

3. Have students look at the flyers. Play the role of Student A. Call on an above-level student to play the role of Student B. Ask several questions about the prices, quantities, and quality of the food in the flyers. For example:

   A: *How much is cereal at Grandee's?*

   B: *It's $4.50 a box or 2 boxes for $8.*

   A: *How much is cereal at AP Mart?*

   B: *It's $2.99 a box.*

   A: *Which one is more expensive?*

   B: *The cereal at Grandee's is more expensive.*

   A: *Which one is more nutritious?*

   B: *The cereal at Grandee's is more nutritious.*

4. Tell students they have 10 minutes and $40 to make a shopping list for food at one of the two markets.

5. Circulate during the activity to correct students' comparative statements as they talk about the two supermarkets and help them with computing the cost of the food.

6. Have the pairs show their shopping lists to each other and explain their choices.

Multilevel Option

Above-Level: If pairs finish the activity before others, have them write a commercial for one of the supermarkets. When the rest of the class is finished with the comparison shopping activity, they can perform their commercials for the class.

Comparison Shopping: *Compare Food Ads*

AP MART

Super Sales! This Week Only!

Lettuce 2 for $5

Fielding's Yogurt 12 oz. 10 for $5

Sweet Crisp Cereal $2.99 18 oz. box

Country Kitchen Chicken Soup 3 for $5 $1.99 each 10 oz. can

Home Farm Eggs $2.25 / Dozen

Sales Prices for this Week

Grandee's Foods

Heart Health Cereal — Complete Cereal — 18 oz. box 2 for $8 $4.50 each

Grandee's fresh bread (24 oz. loaf) 2 for $5

Yogo Yogurt — Sunny Farms Yogurt — 12 oz. 65¢ each

Lettuce $1.99 a head

Grandee's Brand Chicken Soup 12 oz. can $1.75 a can

Kernal's Rice 2 lb bag $4.50 RICE

Ice Cream — Bennett's Ice Cream $2.88 pint

Shopping List for	
_____ (name of supermarket)	
Food	**Price**
(not more than $40) total:	

Build a Sentence: Much *and* Many

Grouping Pairs
Target Language Quantifiers with plural nouns and non-count nouns
Materials Activity Master 49
Class Time 15 minutes

Teacher Preparation

- Copy Activity Master 49, one for each pair of students.

- Cut each copy into 14 cards. Clip each set of cards together.

Procedure

1. Put students in like-ability pairs. Give a set of cards to each pair.

2. Tell Student A to shuffle the cards. Have Student B put the cards face up on his or her desk.

3. Explain that students are going to take turns creating sentences using the cards. They need to always use a "beginning" card with one of the four "There" cards and either the "rice" or "tomatoes" card. Also, point out to them that the cards will be re-used.

4. Model the activity. Assemble a sentence and read it aloud: *There aren't many tomatoes.*

5. Write the sentence on the board. Tell students to assemble the sentence with their cards.

6. Tell students to replace the word cards and assemble another sentence and write it down. Try to have them find all 15 combinations.

7. Circulate during the activity to make sure students' written sentences are correct.

Multilevel Option

Pre-level: Allow pre-level students to work together to create and write the sentences instead of taking turns for each task.

Answer Key

Possible sentences:
There are many tomatoes.
There aren't many tomatoes.
There are a lot of tomatoes.
There aren't a lot of tomatoes.
There are some tomatoes.
There aren't any tomatoes.
There are a few tomatoes.
There's a lot of rice.
There isn't a lot of rice.
There's a little rice.
There isn't much rice.
There's some rice.
There isn't any rice.
There's rice.
There are tomatoes.

Build a Sentence: Much *and* Many

There are	many	rice.
There's	much	tomatoes.
There isn't	some	a few
There aren't	a lot of	any
	a little	enough

Unit 10 • Review

Board Game: *Food*

Grouping	Groups of 4
Target Language	Identify food containers and quantities, nutrition information, compare foods
Materials	Activity Master 50, a coin, two markers for each group
Class Time	20 minutes

Teacher Preparation

Copy Activity Master 50, one for every four students.

Procedure

1. Put students in like-ability pairs. Each pair is a team. Put two teams together to play the game. Give each group of 4 a copy of Activity Master 50, a coin, and two markers.

2. Explain that students are going to play a board game. Here are the rules:

   • Pair 1 flips a coin to move. *Heads* means the team moves the marker ahead two squares and *tails* means the team moves their marker ahead one square.

   • Pair 1 moves the marker to a square. Student A reads the question aloud. Student B answers with true information. Pair 2 listens to make sure Pair 1's answer is appropriate and correct.

   • If Pair 1's answer is correct, Pair 2 takes a turn.

   • If Pair 1's answer is incorrect, Pair 1 moves the marker back one square, and Pair 2 takes a turn.

   • If a pair lands on a square that already has a marker on it, the pair gets to move forward one square.

   • The first pair to reach FINISH wins.

3. Circulate during the activity to make sure students' answers are correct.

Multilevel Option

Allow the pairs of students 10 minutes to read all the lines on the game board and look in the unit of the Student Book to take some notes to help them during the game. This will help the pre-level student prepare for the challenge of this game.

Answer Key

1. 12
2. *Possible answers:* cereal, crackers, cookies
3. *Any four of the following:* carbohydrates, cholesterol, fiber, protein, sodium, sugar
6. *Possible answers:* soup, tuna fish, tomatoes, fruit, baked beans
7. *Possible answers:* meatloaf, hamburger
8. *Possible answers:* potato chips, oranges, rice
9. Roast chicken: It has less cholesterol and fat.
10. *Possible answers:* soda, oil, wine
11. *Possible answers:* Your heart beats faster; you have more energy; you feel more awake; you may feel nervous and irritable; it can give you a headache or stomachache.
12. *Possible answers:* French fries, onion rings, cole slaw
14. *Possible answers:* mayonnaise, jelly, tomato sauce

Board Game: *Food*

START	**1** How many eggs are in a dozen? →	**2** Which foods come in a box? (Name three.) →	**3** What are four nutrients in food? ↓
7 What is a main dish? (Give two examples.) ↓	**6** Which foods come in a can? (Name three.) ←	**5** What's important to you when you buy food? ←	**4** Which food do you like more: homemade food or fast food? Why? ←
8 Which foods come in a bag? (Name three.) →	**9** Which is better for your health: fried chicken or roast chicken? (Give two reasons.) →	**10** Which foods come in a bottle? (Name three.) →	**11** What are two effects of caffeine? ↓
FINISH	**14** Which foods come in a jar? (Name three.) ←	**13** Which food do you like more: fruit or ice cream? Why? ←	**12** What is a side dish? (Give two examples.) ←

Information Gap: *A Dangerous Dinner*

Grouping Pairs
Target Language *Wh-* questions in the present continuous, medical emergencies
Materials Activity Master 51
Class Time 20 minutes

Teacher Preparation

• Copy Activity Master 51, one for every two students.

• Cut each copy into two parts. Clip together Card A and Card B.

Procedure

1. Put students in like-ability pairs. Give a copy of Card A to Student A and a copy of Card B to Student B in each pair.

2. Explain that students are going to ask and answer questions to complete the story.

3. Write *Where _____?* on the board. Have students complete the question for the first item, *Where are Bob and Nancy having dinner?* Then model the activity. Play the part of Student A. Call on an above-level student to play the part of Student B:

   A: *Where are Bob and Nancy having dinner?*

   B: *They're having dinner at a restaurant.*

   A: *A restaurant?*

   B: *Yes.*

   Instruct all Student As to write *a restaurant* in the blank on line 1 of their card.

4. Have groups continue the activity. Tell students that they should not show each other their cards.

5. Circulate during the activity to help students form the correct questions and to make sure they do not show their partners their cards until the end of the activity.

6. After the pairs have shared all their information, have them compare their cards to check their information. The stories on Cards A and B should be the same.

Multilevel Options

Pre-level: Have pre-level students meet with students who have the same card. (Card A students sit together. Card B students sit together.) Have the students work together to write the questions for each blank on their card. Then have them meet with a person with a different card to ask and answer the questions.

Above-level: Have above-level students fold the question words under their card so they have to form the question independently.

Extension

After the class finishes the activity, ask students: *Have you or anyone you know ever had an allergic reaction? Was it this serious?*

Information Gap: *A Dangerous Dinner*

Card A: *A Dangerous Dinner*

1. Bob and Nancy are having dinner at _____.   **where**
2. Bob is eating rice with a little egg and peanuts.   **what**
3. Suddenly _____ is having trouble breathing!   **who**
4. "What's happening?" the waitress asks.
5. "He's having _____!" Nancy says.   **what**
6. Nancy is looking for something in Bob's coat pocket.   **who**
7. She is holding _____.   **what**
8. She is pressing the pen into his leg.   **where**
9. _____ is getting calmer.   **who**
10. The waitress is calling 911.   **who**
11. ___ _____ is coming.   **what**
12. Bob is going to the hospital.   **where**
13. Bob was lucky. Nancy found his EpiPen. She saved his life.

Card B: *A Dangerous Dinner*

1. Bob and Nancy are having dinner at a restaurant.   **where**
2. Bob is eating _____.   **what**
3. Suddenly Bob is having trouble breathing!   **who**
4. "What's happening?" the waitress asks.
5. "He's having an allergic reaction!" Nancy says.   **what**
6. _____ looking for something in Bob's coat pocket.   **who**
7. She is holding a small pen.   **what**
8. She is pressing the pen into his _____.   **where**
9. Bob is getting calmer.   **who**
10. _____ is calling 911.   **who**
11. The ambulance is coming.   **what**
12. Bob is going to _____.   **where**
13. Bob was lucky. Nancy found his EpiPen. She saved his life.

Unit 11 • Lesson 6

Mix and Match: *Conversations*

Grouping Pairs
Target Language Identifying medical emergencies, calling 911 to report an emergency, describing an emergency
Materials Activity Master 52
Class Time 20 minutes

Teacher Preparation

- Copy Activity Master 52, one for each pair of students.

- Cut each copy into 16 cards. The white cards are Speaker A and the gray cards are Speaker B.

- Clip each set of cards together.

Procedure

1. Put students in like-ability pairs. Give a set of cards to each pair.

2. Tell Student A to shuffle the white cards and Student B to shuffle the gray cards. Have students put their cards face up on their desks.

3. Explain that students are going to work together to make three different dialogues with the cards. Tell students that Speaker A always begins the conversation (white cards).

4. Model the activity. Pull out a Speaker A card with a question, for example: *9-1-1. What's your emergency?* Ask the class to look for the response in the B cards (gray cards). When a student finds it, have the student call it out so everyone can find it. *A woman fell down the stairs. I think she's unconscious.*

5. Tell students to continue in pairs to find the next line.

6. Circulate during the activity to make sure students' matched dialogues are correct.

   Note: Refer to the activity master to see the dialogues in their correct order.

Multilevel Option

Pre-level: Identify the first card in each of the three conversations to scaffold the activity for pre-level students.

Mix and Match: *Conversations*

A: 9-1-1. What's your emergency?

B: A woman fell down the stairs. I think she's unconscious.

A: What's the location of the emergency?

B: We're at 324 Robson Street.

A: An ambulance is on its way. What's your name?

B: I'm Parviz Patel.

A: Mr. Patel, please stay on the line until the ambulance gets there.

A: Did you hear what happened yesterday?

B: No. What happened?

A: There was a bank robbery

B: That's terrible. Was anybody hurt?

A: Yes. Two bank employees went to the hospital.

A: Traffic was terrible this morning. What was going on?

B: There was a construction accident.

A: Oh my gosh. Were there any injuries?

B: No, luckily no one was hurt. But there was a big traffic jam.

Picture-based Story: *Cooking in the Kitchen*

Grouping	Pairs and then whole class
Target Language	Causes of home injuries
Materials	Activity Master 53
Class Time	25 minutes

Teacher Preparation

Copy Activity Master 53, one for each student.

Procedure

1. Give a copy of Activity Master 53 to each student.

2. Explain that students are going to write a story based on the pictures.

3. Put students in cross-ability pairs to discuss the questions on Activity Master 53.

4. Have students report their ideas to the class. Make sure students understand the scenes:

   (1) Lucy and Park are cooking. Lucy is not being careful at the stove.

   (2) Lucy burned herself. Park is calling 911.

5. Ask the class: *What's the story?* Have the class develop a <u>general</u> story line orally. Write key vocabulary words on the board.

6. Have students return to working in pairs to write a draft of their story. Circulate around the classroom, helping students with their writing. Encourage students to add details to their stories by asking additional questions such as: *What are they cooking? What are they talking about? How did the accident happen?*

7. As pairs finish their stories, put them together with another partner to share their stories and give one another feedback.

8. Have students write a final copy of their story to submit to you for your corrections and feedback.

Multilevel Option

Above-level: Have above-level students be the scribes in their pairs.

Extension

Have students role-play the conversation between Park and the 911 operator.

Picture-based Story: *Cooking in the Kitchen*

- What are Lucy and Park doing?
- Can you see any safety hazards?

- What happened?
- What is Park doing?
- What happens next?

1. **PAIRS: Discuss the questions under each picture.**

2. **CLASS: Tell the story to the teacher. Write down the new vocabulary.**

3. **PAIRS: Write your story together.**

Put in Order: *A Traffic Violation*

Grouping	Pairs
Target Language	Traffic violations, responding to a police officer
Materials	Activity Master 54
Class Time	15 minutes

Teacher Preparation

- Copy Activity Master 54, one for each pair of students.

- Cut each copy into 11 cards.

- Clip each set of cards together.

Procedure

1. Put students in like-ability pairs. Give a set of cards to each pair.

2. Tell students to shuffle the cards and put all of them face up on their desks.

3. Explain that students are going to work together to put in order a story of a traffic violation.

4. Model the activity. Pull out the first card: *A driver runs a red light.* Have all students find that card. It has the number 1 on it. Then ask: *What happens next?* When a student finds the next card, *The driver sees a police car following him*, have the student read the card aloud to the class so everyone can find it.

5. Tell students to continue in their pairs to put the story in order.

6. Circulate during the activity to make sure students' are putting the story in the correct order.

   Note: Refer to the activity master to see the story in its correct order.

Multilevel Option

Pre-level: Write the number on several of the cards to provide pre-level learners with some scaffolding.

Extension

Have three student volunteers mime the story card by card. One person narrates the cards as two students role-play the driver and the officer.

Put in Order: *A Traffic Violation*

1. A driver runs a red light.

The driver sees a police car following him.

The driver pulls over to the right and stops his car.

The driver waits in his car for the police officer to speak to him.

The officer asks the driver for his license, registration, and proof of insurance.

The officer takes the driver's documents back to the police car.

The officer checks the documents carefully.

The officer returns to the driver's car.

The officer gives the driver his documents and a ticket.

The officer says the driver can leave.

The driver starts his car and drives away

Board Game: *Emergencies*

Grouping	Groups of 4
Target Language	identify medical emergencies, talk about fire safety procedures, respond to police officer's instructions
Materials	Activity Master 55, a coin, two markers for each group
Class Time	20 minutes

Teacher Preparation

Copy Activity Master 55, one for every four students.

Procedure

1. Put students in like-ability pairs. Each pair is a team. Put two teams together to play the game. Give each group of 4 a copy of Activity Master 55, a coin, and two markers.

2. Explain that students are going to play a board game. Here are the rules:

   • Pair 1 flips a coin to move. *Heads* means the team moves the marker ahead two squares and *tails* means the team moves their marker ahead one square.

   • Pair 1 moves the marker to a square. Student A reads the question aloud. Student B answers with true information. Pair 2 listens to make sure Pair 1's answer is appropriate and correct.

   • If Pair 1's answer is correct, Pair 2 takes a turn.

   • If Pair 1's answer is incorrect, Pair 1 moves the marker back one square, and Pair 2 takes a turn.

   • If a pair lands on a square that already has a marker on it, the pair gets to move forward one square.

   • The first pair to reach FINISH wins.

3. Circulate during the activity to make sure students' answers are correct.

Multilevel Option

Pre-level: Allow the pairs of students 10 minutes to read all the lines on the game board and look in the unit of the Student Book to take some notes to help them during the game. This will help the pre-level student prepare for the challenge of this game.

Answer Key

1. *Possible answers:* someone is having a heart attack, is having an allergic reaction, swallowed poison

2. *Possible answers:* someone swallowed poison, is having trouble breathing, is choking, is having a heart attack

3. *Possible answers:* Leave the home immediately; touch a door before opening it; call 911 when you get out; don't go back in the home.

4. *Possible answers:* too many plugs in an electrical outlet, an electrical cord under a rug, no window exit, a heater close to a curtain

5. Wait in the car.

6. fire extinguisher, smoke alarm, fire escape plan

7. *Possible answers:* What is the emergency? Where are you? What's the location of the emergency? What's your name?

8. *Possible answers:* turn pot handles inward; don't wear loose clothing

9. a plan for exiting your home if there is a fire

10. your license, registration, and proof of insurance

11. *Possible answers:* running a red light, speeding, tailgating, not wearing a seat belt

13. *Possible answers:* falls, poisonings, burns, choking

14. Keep medicine and cleaning supplies away from children; keep medicines in their original containers

Board Game: *Emergencies*

	1	**2**	**3**
START	What are three medical emergencies? →	When should you call 911? Name four emergency situations. →	There is a fire in your home. What should you do? (Name four tips.) ↓
7 What are three questions a 911 operator asks a caller? ↓	**6** What are three things to make your home safe from fire? ←	**5** A police officer pulls you over. What's the first thing you should do? ←	**4** What are four fire hazards in a home? ←
8 You are cooking in your kitchen. What are two safety tips? →	**9** What is a fire escape plan? →	**10** A police officer pulls over a driver. What documents does he / she ask for? →	**11** What are four traffic violations? ↓
FINISH	**14** What are two home safety tips to keep you safe from poisoning? ←	**13** What are three common causes of home injuries? ←	**12** What are the *cross streets* at your school? ←

Build a Sentence: *Work Responsibilities*

Grouping Pairs
Target Language Policies at work, work responsibilities, expressions of necessity and prohibition
Materials Activity Master 56
Class Time 15 minutes

Teacher Preparation

- Copy Activity Master 56, one for each pair of students.

- Cut each copy into 20 cards. The white cards are sentence beginnings and the gray cards are sentence endings.

  Note: You may want to start with only the first five pairs.

- Clip each set of cards together.

Procedure

1. Put students in like-ability pairs. Give a set of cards to each pair.

2. Tell Student A to shuffle the white cards and Student B to shuffle the gray cards. Have students put their cards face up on their desks.

3. Explain that students are going to work together to make ten (or five) correct sentences with the cards. Tell students that the white cards are sentence beginnings and the gray cards are sentence endings.

4. Model the activity. Assemble a white card and a gray card into a correct sentence and read it aloud: *All new employees have to go to the orientation meeting.*

5. Write the sentence on the board. Tell students to assemble the sentence with their cards.

6. Tell students to continue to assemble correct sentences.

7. Circulate during the activity to make sure students' matched sentences are correct.

   Note: Refer to the activity master to see the correct sentence matches.

Multilevel Option

Pre-level: Give pre-level students only the first five pairs of cards so that they have fewer choices to consider as they match the cards. When they finish the first half of the cards, give them the second half.

Variation

Mixer: Use one copy of Activity Master 56. Give each student a card at random. Have students walk around the classroom. They continually say their half of the sentence until they find the matching half. If there are more than 20 students, use two copies of Activity Master 56.

Build a Sentence: *Work Responsibilities*

1. All new employees have to go	to the orientation meeting.
2. All employees must wear	latex gloves.
3. Everyone must eat	in the break room.
4. Employees must not be	late.
5. Employees must wash	hands.
6. Employees have to follow	the health and safety rules.
7. Employees must report	problems to the manager.
8. Employees can't trade	shifts.
9. All employees have to clock	in and out.
10. Employees can't make	personal calls at work.

Unit 12 • Lesson 4

Future 2 pages 232–233

Picture-based Story: *The Paycheck*

Grouping	Pairs and whole class
Target Language	Talking about a pay stub, simple past tense
Materials	Activity Master 57
Class Time	25 minutes

Teacher Preparation

Copy Activity Master 57, one for each student.

Procedure

1. Give a copy of Activity Master 57 to each student.

2. Explain that students are going to write a story based on the pictures.

3. Put students in cross-ability pairs to discuss the questions about the pictures on Activity Master 57.

4. Have students report their ideas to the class. Make sure students understand the scenes:

   (1) It's pay day. Max is picking up his paycheck at work.

   (2) Max is surprised. The check is not in the correct amount.

   (3) The pay stub says that Max worked 42 hours last week.

   (4) Max goes back to the office. He's telling the person that he didn't get paid for all the overtime hours he worked.

5. Ask the class: *What's the story?* Have students describe each picture. Write key vocabulary words on the board.

6. Have students return to working in pairs to write a draft of their story. Circulate around the classroom, helping students with their writing.

7. As students finish their stories, put them together with another pair to share their stories and give one another feedback.

8. Have students write a final copy of their story to submit to you for your corrections and feedback.

Multilevel Option

Above-level: Have above-level students be the scribes in their pairs.

114 Future 2 Multilevel Communicative Activities

Picture-based Story: *The Paycheck*

- What day is today?
- What is Max doing?

- Is Max happy with his check?

Description	Hours	Earnings
Regular	40	$400.00
Overtime	2	$30.00
Total Gross Pay		$430.00

- How many hours did Max work?

- What is Max saying?
- What happens next?

1. **PAIRS: Discuss the questions under each picture.**

2. **CLASS: Tell the story to the teacher. Write down the new vocabulary.**

3. **PAIRS: Write your story together.**

Information Gap: *Who takes care of the patients?*

Grouping	Whole-class mixer
Target Language	Information questions with *Who / Where / What*
Materials	Activity Master 58
Class Time	20 minutes

Teacher Preparation

Cut each copy into two parts. Clip together Schedule A and Schedule B.

Procedure

1. Put students in like-ability pairs. Give a copy of Schedule A to Student A and a copy of Schedule B to Student B in each pair.

2. Explain that students are going to fill in the missing information in their schedules by asking each other questions with *who*, *where*, and *what*.

3. Write *Who* _____? on the board. Have Student As complete the question for their first item, *Who does Wilma supervise?* You may want to point out that the question is about the object of the sentence so it uses the auxiliary verb *does*. Play the part of Student A. Call on an above-level student to play the part of Student B:

   A: *Who does Wilma supervise?*

   B: *She supervises the aides.*

   A: *The aides?*

   B: *Yes.*

   Instruct all Student As to write *aides* on the first line of their schedules.

4. Continue to model the activity. Write *Who* _____? on the board. Have Student Bs complete the question for their first item, *Who takes care of patients on the first floor?* You may want to point out that the question is about the subject of the sentence so it does not use the auxiliary verb. Play the part of Student B. Call on an above-level student to play the part of Student A:

   B: *Who takes care of patients on the first floor?*

   A: *Krista takes care of the patients on the first floor.*

   B: *Krista?*

   A: *Yes.*

   Instruct all Student Bs to write *Krista* on the first line of their information cards.

5. Have pairs continue the activity. Tell students that they should take turns asking the names and occupations of the people on their cards.

6. Circulate during the activity to help students with their question formation and to make sure they do not show their partners their schedules until the end of the activity.

7. When pairs have filled in all the information, have partners compare schedules to check their information. The information on both cards should be the same.

Multilevel Option

Pre-level: Have all students meet with classmates who have the same card. (Card A students sit together. Card B students sit together.) Have students work together to write the questions for each blank on their card. Then have them meet with a person with a different card to ask and answer the questions. This helps pre-level students by focusing on one task at a time.

Information Gap: *Who takes care of the patients?*

Schedule A	Grove Care Center First Shift—Tuesday, February 2	
Position	**Duties**	**Location**
Head Nurse: Wilma	supervise _____	whole building
Nurse's Aide: Krista	take care of patients	on the 1st floor
Nurse's Aide: _____	take care of patients	on the 2nd floor
Food Service Aide: Tim	assist patients with _____	in the dining hall
Food Service Aide: Jen	assist patients with snacks	_____
Receptionist: Pamela	greet _____, sort mail	at the main desk
Counselor: _____	see patients, communicate with families	in the counselor's office

Schedule B	Grove Care Center First Shift—Tuesday, February 2	
Position	**Duties**	**Location**
Supervising Nurse: Wilma	supervise aides	whole building
Nurse's Aide: _____	take care of patients	on the 1st floor
Nurse's Aide: Marsha	take care of patients	on the 2nd floor
Food Service Aide: Tim	assist patients with lunch	_____
Food Service Aide: Jen	assist patients with _____	on the 2nd floor
Receptionist: Pamela	greet visitors, sort _____	at the main desk
Counselor: Bill	see patients, communicate with _____	_____

Mix and Match: *Conversations*

Grouping Pairs
Target Language Asking about policies at work, asking about work schedules, requesting a schedule change
Materials Activity Master 59
Class Time 20 minutes

Teacher Preparation

- Copy Activity Master 59, one for each pair of students.

- Cut each copy into 14 cards. The white cards are Speaker A and the gray cards are Speaker B.

- Clip each set of cards together.

Procedure

1. Put students in like-ability pairs. Give a set of cards to each pair.

2. Tell Student A to shuffle the white cards and Student B to shuffle the gray cards. Have students put their cards faceup on their desks.

3. Explain that students are going to work together to make three different dialogues with the cards. Tell students that Speaker A always begins the conversation (white cards).

4. Model the activity. Pull out a Speaker A card with a question, for example, *Can I ask you a question?* Ask the class to look for the response in the B cards (gray cards). When a student finds it, have the student call it out so everyone can find it. *Sure. What do you want to know?*

5. Tell students to continue in pairs to find the next line.

6. Circulate during the activity to make sure students' matched dialogues are correct.

   Note: Refer to the activity master to see the dialogues in their correct order.

Multilevel Option

Pre-level: Identify the first card in each of the three conversations to scaffold the activity for pre-level students.

Mix and Match: *Conversations*

A: Can I ask you a question?	B: Sure. What do you want to know?
A: Am I allowed to make personal calls at work?	B: No, you aren't. You have to turn off your phone when you clock in.
A: Can I ask you a favor? I'm on the schedule for Friday, but I can't come in.	B: Oh. Why not?
A: I have to pick up my aunt at the airport. Can you take my shift for me?	B: What time do you start?
A: My shift begins at 2:00.	B: I'm sorry. I can't cover your hours. I have plans for Friday evening.
A: Can I speak to you for a minute? I need to talk to you about my schedule.	B: OK. Right now you work in the evenings, right?
A: Yes. But my wife's work schedule changed. Could I change to mornings?	B: Let me look at the schedule. A lot of people need morning hours. I'll get back to you.

Board Game: *Work Schedules*

Grouping	Groups of 4
Target Language	Information questions with *What / Which / When / Where / Who*, expressions of necessity and prohibition
Materials	Activity Master 60, a coin, two markers for each group
Class Time	20 minutes

Teacher Preparation

Copy Activity Master 60, one for every four students.

Procedure

1. Put students in like-ability pairs. Each pair is a team. Put two teams together to play the game. Give each group of 4 a copy of Activity Master 60, a coin, and two markers.

2. Explain that students are going to play a board game. Here are the rules:

   • Pair 1 flips a coin to move. *Heads* means the team moves the marker ahead two squares and *tails* means the team moves their marker ahead one square.

   • Pair 1 moves the marker to a square. Student A reads the question aloud. Student B answers with true information about the work schedule. Pair 2 listens to make sure Pair 1's answer is appropriate and correct.

   • If Pair 1's answer is correct, Pair 2 takes a turn.

   • If Pair 1's answer is incorrect, Pair 1 moves the marker back one square, and Pair 2 takes a turn.

   • If a pair lands on a square that already has a marker on it, the pair gets to move forward one square.

   • The first pair to reach FINISH wins.

3. Circulate during the activity to make sure students' answers are correct.

Extension

If some pairs finish before others, have them write out their work or school schedule and have their partner ask questions about it. For example:

Extension

If some pairs finish before others, have them write out their work or school schedule and have their partner ask questions about it. For example:

Where do you work?

When do you study?

Answer Key
1. Who works as a stock clerk? Jack
2. What time does Carla's shift begin? At 3:30
3. Who works full-time? Linda
4. Can employees trade shifts? No, they can't. They have to tell the manager.
5. What does Linda do? She'a cashier.
6. Where do Linda, Carla, Ron, and Jack work? At Mayfield Clothing Store.
7. Which days does Ron have off? Wednesday, Thursday, Friday, and Saturday
8. Which shift do Rona and Carla work? The afternoon shift (from 3:30 to 9:30)
9. Who works part-time? Jack, Ron, and Carla
10. When does Linda work? From 10:00 to 6:00, Monday to Friday.
11. Who does Carla work with in the afternoon? Linda
12. Which days does Linda work? Monday to Friday
13. What time does Ron's shift end? At 9:30.
14. Who works on Monday? Jack, Ron, and Linda
15. Can employees take a 30-minute break? No, they can't.

Board Game: *Work Schedules*

START

FINISH

1 who / work / as a stock clerk?

2 what time / Carla's shift / begin?

3 who / work / full-time?

4 can / employees / trade shifts?

5 what / Linda / do?

6 where / Linda, Carla, Ron, and Jack / work?

7 which days / Ron / have off?

8 which shift / Ron and Carla / work?

9 who / work / part time?

10 when / Linda / work?

11 who / Carla / work with / in the afternoon?

12 which days / Linda / work?

13 what time / Ron's shift / end?

14 who / work / on Monday?

15 can / employees / take / a 30-minute break?

Mayfield Clothing Store
Week of 7/7–7/13

	Mon.	Tues.	Wed.	Thurs.	Fri.	Sat.	Sun.
Jack stock clerk	9:30–3:30		9:30–3:30	9:30–3:30		9:30–3:30	
Ron sales associate	3:30–9:30	3:30–9:30					3:30–9:30
Linda cashier	10:00–6:00	10:00–6:00	10:00–6:00	10:00–6:00	10:00–6:00		
Carla sales associate			3:30–9:30	3:30–9:30	3:30–9:30	3:30–9:30	

Remember: Tell the manager when you trade shifts. Breaks are only 15 minutes long!